Amanda Susa.

A dog's life in Italy

europe books

© 2023 **Europe Books**| London
www.europebooks.co.uk | info@europebooks.co.uk

ISBN 9791220138956
First edition: June 2023

BUILD

UNIVERSES

A dog's life in Italy

For my daughter Sara Victoria

*With special thanks to my family, especially to my mum,
who was the first to read my story.*

CONTENTS

Hello 13

My new family gets bigger 17

Where I sleep 21

My doggie friends 29

Learning the rules 35

My Nana 41

My Toys 47

Hen pecked 53

Cleaning day 57

The clean and smelly dog 59

The Uninvited Friend 63

The dog with no name 67

Living with a teenager 69

A different Christmas 77

A dog is a man's best friend 81

The devastating news 87

My daily routine 91

The coronavirus time 105

The rescued Romanian dog 109

A great surprise 111

Pandemic dogs 113

The pandemic continues 115

Friends and fights......................................117

A meeting with a new dog 123

My predecessor 125

The three-legged dog................................133

Family life 137

The yoga dog...143

The unwanted birthday present 147

Time to say goodbye for now....................151

Hello

Hello, my name's Tyson, that is pronounced "ties on", for example, the school children look very smart with their ties on. I am a small, brown medium sized dog with a small head, brown eyes that are not very big, small ears that are lovely and soft, a face which resembles a fox and a long bushy tail. I am not a particular breed but a mixture, or a Heinz dog as they say, but I have heard that I have some terrier blood in me. I'm very proud of that as terriers are very intelligent! I would also just like to mention that I'm not one of those silent dogs that never have anything to say. No, I love communicating to humans with a woof, woof, woof. If somebody says something to me, *"wo, wo, woooo"*, I reply, or I grunt or snort. I even make a noise when I'm sleeping as I snore or make whimpering sounds as I dream.

Anyway, this is my story, told by me, of my life with my human family. I am a very, very lucky dog to live with wonderful, caring people, in a beautiful home in the countryside of Massa Lubrense, near the well-known town of Sorrento in the south of Italy.

So, let's begin!

I was born on a sunny November's day together with my brothers and sisters to a warm, caring mummy. I don't really remember a lot about the first few weeks of my life except that there were always warm bodies to cuddle up to, my mum or brothers or sisters, and lots of tasty milk. Then, sometimes I was picked up and cuddled by humans, who were very gentle to me and also gave me and my siblings names.

So, in actual fact my first name was Lotti. I don't know why I was given this name, but in Italian "lottare" means to struggle, so maybe I had a struggle to get to suck milk from my mummy. When you are part of a big family there is always a lot of competition, and in my case my other brothers and sisters were always there before me drinking milk from our mummy, leaving me no room. Anyway, the important thing was that I survived and was growing up strong and healthy and was getting ready to move on to a new home. I couldn't stay at my birth home because there would be far too many of us doggies. Consequently, in those later weeks I saw some of my brothers and sisters leaving us to go to their new home and I wondered when my time would come.

Perhaps it would be soon! I remember one day a very pretty girl with lovely suntanned skin and curly, brown hair came to see us puppies. We were all very excited and wagged our tails furiously to get her attention. She crouched down and looked at all of us, saying how beautiful we all were, stroking our heads and picking us up to give us a cuddle. When it was my time, my heart melted with joy. She had such a lovely scent on her that I licked her face all over, and when her beautiful, dark brown eyes looked deeply into my fox-like eyes, I knew that we had fallen in love.

"I am the one for you, take me to your home!", I yapped at her, but what happened? She carefully put me down, stood up and went away without me. I couldn't believe it, I was heartbroken, I really wanted to be with her. So, sadly it was back to cuddling up to mummy, which was nice, but I was growing up and getting to be a big doggie and wanted to leave my birth home and have a new life with new adventures.

The next day, the lovely girl with the curly, brown hair returned and again was with us all. I expected she had come to take one of my brothers or sisters away with her, so although I was really happy to see her and smell that lovely perfume again, I kept my distance as she was playing happily with my siblings.

All of a sudden, her gaze came to me as she exclaimed that I was the one she wanted! She picked me up, carried me to the door, said goodbye to everyone else, and off we went. It was the month of January so a bit nippy, conse-

quently I needed a little jacket on.

I had been chosen. I was so happy I had to be careful not to wriggle too much in her arms and fall to the ground.

My luck had come, I was going to a new home with a new family. I was so excited; my early puppyhood had finished, and I was about to embark on a new life where I had the extremely important role of being:

"The family pet dog!"

My new family gets bigger

After arriving at my new home, I discovered that my new family was not very big. In fact, there were only two people in it: Victoria, the lovely suntanned girl, with the curly, brown hair who had come to fetch me from my birth home, and her dad Francesco, who always seemed to wear a hat both outside and also inside the house. He seemed quite cheerful and very happy to meet me, he smiled at me, stroked me, picked me up just with one hand because I was so little and his hands quite big, gave me a cuddle and talked to me.

So, it was easy for me to understand straight away that he was a doggie person, that is a person who loves dogs. You know, we dogs have a special ability to sense if a human is an animal lover and feels comfortable with us, or if, on the other hand, a person feels uneasy in our presence. Anyway, I replied to the pleasure of meeting him by wagging my tail excitedly

and licking his face all over. When he put me down on the floor, I also noticed he was quite robust, so he obviously ate well. That was a good sign of him tucking into delicious, tasty meals and maybe lots of yummy titbits for me!! Life was going to be just amazing!

Their house was a ground floor apartment with an enormous garden, just one problem though, I couldn't get in. To get to the big, wooden front door there was a very high step, well high for me, my legs were just too short to get up it. Therefore, Victoria had to lift me up and then she showed me around what was now MY house, which was very pleasant and quite spacious.

Then she showed me my bed which she had already prepared for me, with a

soft, warm blanket to make it nice and cosy, and inside there was a soft toy for me to cuddle up to if I missed my mummy.

Everything was perfect, and I soon got into my new routine with my new family of two.

That is until one day a bit later on when all of this was suddenly disrupted. It was afternoon time, and I was having a peaceful nap in my warm, comfy bed, a little too warm actually, so I stuck my legs up into the air to cool off a bit.

All of a sudden, the front door burst open, making me jump, and a tall lady with short blonde hair marched in. She hadn't even rung the doorbell or knocked!
"How impolite! ", I thought. *"Who on earth are you? How dare you come into my house!"*.

I did my puppy bark and tried to growl as angrily as I could, but it didn't seem to have any effect as she continued to tow into MY house this enormous, rectangular kind of box on wheels, which I had never seen before. She didn't pay any attention to me at all and in fact went out of the house only to return with another object on wheels, more gigantic than the first! I was beside myself. It was my job to protect my home and my humans, Victoria and Francesco against this unwelcome imposter, but I wasn't winning.

Francesco and Victoria were not helping me at all, and this strange lady did not seem to be at all perturbed. I was doing my utmost, barking and snarling, prepared to risk my life to save my family from harm. It was all exhausting, but then also frightening when this woman suddenly looked at me straight in the eye and said:

-Heyyy, how dare you bark at me! This is MY house!!!-

19

"WHAT???", I thought, *"What is she talking about??? Her house?"*

Now things were getting very confusing, but after she had deposited her things, she knelt down and put her hand out towards me. She had a warm smile on her face and love in her eyes. I was still a bit suspicious of her and frightened, but as she didn't move and was very calm, I eventually quietened down and decided to extend my nose to see what she smelt like. She didn't move her hand until I had had a good sniff, then very slowly and gently she began to touch my head and my ears and my body smiling at me lovingly and said:

-Hello, I'm Amy, I live here too with Francesco and Victoria, I'm Francesco's wife and Victoria's mummy. I've been to England to visit my English family and friends, and those big objects on wheels that frightened you are my suitcases that people use when they travel. Aren't you lovely? Let me have a look at you!-

I started to wag my tail and wriggle about. She was not a scary enemy like I had originally thought, but a third member of my family to love and protect like my precious Victoria and Francesco. Suddenly, I could feel my big, warm, dark brown puppy eyes gazing deep into hers, as in my little puppy head I said to myself that I promised to protect her  together with Victoria and Francesco loyally until death do us part.

Where I sleep

It is very important when you adopt a puppy to provide a cosy, comfortable bed. The little puppy has just been separated from its mummy and maybe brothers and sisters, so obviously it will feel alone, cold and perhaps even sad. I remember when I arrived at my new house with Victoria, there was a cosy little basket with a warm blanket and a soft toy for me to cuddle up to, which she had obviously already organized for me. This made me feel secure and warm and I didn't miss my previous family, also because Victoria took time to cuddle me and play with me.

We doggies want to be your family pet, we want to accompany you in the activities that you do, and most importantly we also want company from you. We don't really want to be left alone for long periods of time, even if we have a lovely kennel or basket, or bed. We want to share our lives with you. Of course, to do this, it is essential that we are trained to be obedient, and I will talk about this in more detail in chapter 5.

Getting back to where I sleep, or first of all let's talk about where I used to sleep when I was a puppy. A puppy is like a baby or a young child, full of bounce and energy and then all of sudden in need of a little nap.

Here is an example of when I'd been playing with Victoria, and all of a sudden as she was cuddling me, I was so warm and comfy that I just couldn't keep my eyes open anymore.

Another time I was helping Ami clean and sort out the shoe cupboard, sniffing all the various shoes to discover who they belonged to. Yes, those very big muddy trainers were Francesco's, the very posh shoes with extraordinary high heels smelt like they'd been on Victoria's feet and the plain, lace up boots were Ami's, the ones she wore when she took me for a little walk. I recognized the smell of those very easily, and after playing tug of war with an old sock that Ami and I had found, I suddenly felt exhausted. Fortunately, there was a shoe box on the floor which was just the job for a short kip. Here in this picture, I had just woken up and wondered where I was!!!

Then, when the weather got a little warmer, I was taken to this place where there were small, round stones everywhere, not very comfortable to walk on for my little pads, but these stones got nice and warm, so it was ok to lie on them for a short time. There was also a lot of blue water that came up to me and then went away from me,

22

which was very cold, so I wasn't keen on getting my feet wet at all. This was my first trip to the beach!

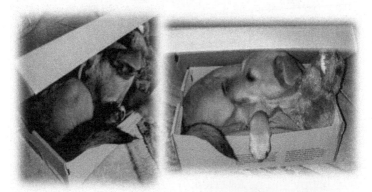

Very nice, but also tiring walking on those pebbles and running away from the sea so as not to get my feet wet. Yet again, I was lucky and found a soft comfy bed, which happened to be Francesco's fishing bag.

When it was bedtime, first of all I had my pyjamas put on for me. They were nothing posh, nothing bought from the pet shop, in fact Ami had made them for me out of Victoria's old neck snood. But they were just the right size, not too big or too tight and were very warm and comfy.

At bedtime I was put into my basket which I understood was only mine and settled down for the night. I was very happy and never cried.

In the morning the first person to get up usually opened the door to let me out and as it's still quite chilly early on left my pyjamas on me. Well, I found it very difficult not to get them dirty while having a stroll around the garden, especially if it was wet, so when I got home Amy had to wash them for me, or even make me a new pair. I don't think she minded too much.

As I got bigger, I kept falling out of my little basket, so of course, it had to be replaced. But what I got next was really ace! Victoria's nana was here to stay, and she bought me a bed especially for dogs, with high sides and a lower part where you could rest your chin, which was very comfy and, in this way, I could see everything that was going on, when I was awake that is!

Plus, the fact it was blue for boys with red racing cars printed on it. It was super dooper. No, I say blue because I'm a boy and blue is the colour for a boy, but some time before this Francesco had bought me a new harness which was PINK! Why had he done this? Apparently, it hadn't even occurred to him! So, I was taken out in this PINK harness. Consequently, when we met other male dogs with their owners, they saw me wearing pink and automatically thought I was a girl, good job Amy used to tell them that I was a boy, otherwise there probably would have been lots of fights.

Can you see the pink harness in this photo?

After many hairy episodes I was given a very smart black harness which went very well with my tan-coloured coat. I am a very handsome boy, you know!!! Only in this photo you can't see my beautiful brown eyes as I've got them shut.

As I've already said, I loved my new bed. Again, it was mine and only mine. If ever I got into trouble like for picking Francesco's sock up off the floor and taking it into the garden and got told off, that's the place I would go. I knew I was safe there. I would walk there, or sometimes if Amy was really cross, (or pretending to be anyway), run there with my tail down between my legs, throw myself down and look to be the saddest dog in the world. It is so important for us dogs to have our own little place to escape to and feel protected.

Unfortunately, though, it is not only mine. When my doggie friend Lilly visits, it's the first place she goes. She comes in, doesn't even say hello to anyone, and makes a bee line for MY bed!! And then me? Where do I have to sleep? On the draughty carpet or mat! Still, I suppose I'm a good friend and really quite a gentleman, so I don't mind if it's for a short time.

This photo shows you a time when I didn't feel like giving up my bed to Lilly and made her lie on the carpet. I was pretending to be asleep, but can you see I've got one eye open.

I loved my bed. Sometimes when I was bored though I chewed it. I got told off for doing that because then Francesco had to sew it up. Other times I took it into the garden and pretended it was my rag, shaking it from one side to another... well, it was a good way of giving it a clean, getting the dust off.

However, eventually it did start to look a bit grubby, and Amy said it was time for a new one. Francesco went out and what did he come back with? A kind of house!!! It was like a basket but with a roof over it, so when I went in nobody could see me, so I could sleep, dream and snore without getting disturbed. It was much warmer too. I loved it, and guess what? So did Lilly when she came to visit.

And now I'll tell you about how Lilly came into my life and my other doggie friends.

My doggie friends

I really settled well into my new home and with my new family, and to top it all I had also made a doggie friend. Who could ask for more? Her name was Lilly and she lived just sort of next door to us, though to get to her house, you first of all had to go through my garden and then through Lilly's.

The very first time I met her was at my house, apparently, she had often come for a visit before my arrival and so she must have been a little surprised when one day she confidently walked into the kitchen and found me there. Straight away though, she wagged her tail showing me that she wasn't a threat but wanted to be friendly, sniffed me all over and obviously thought I was lovely and that I could be a great playmate for her and in fact we hit it off together immediately. Some people thought we were mother and son, or brother and sister maybe, because we did actually look a little similar to each other especially

when I was a puppy and was smaller than her, but since then I've become fully grown, my legs have become longer, so now I'm taller than her, and we've also got different shaped eyes and ears.

So, she wasn't a relative or a girlfriend but became a kind of babysitter to me when I was little. When Ami had her lessons to do and Lilly was with us Ami was happier because she knew Lilly would look after me, play with me in the house or in the garden, and in that way I wouldn't interrupt her lessons and get myself into trouble.

With time our friendship just got deeper and deeper, when Lilly wasn't at my house, I would venture to her house and play with her there and also be a bit of a pet to her human family.

There were also another two dogs who lived with Lilly, one was an old lady called Bella, and the other one was Chestnut, who had so much brown, shaggy hair on her body and head that you couldn't even see her eyes. They both became my friends too. I was made to feel very welcome

at their house and actually even stayed there numerous times when Ami, Francesco and Victoria went on holiday. I really loved sleeping with Chestnut, she was so warm to cuddle up to with all that hair. How funny she looked during the summer though, when she had it all shaved off!! I'm glad I didn't have to go through that!

Sometimes in the morning Chestnut and Bella would come to my garden on their little walk and I would join them, it was as if they had purposely come to call for me. A wander round the garden together, maybe even an exciting cat chase, though I knew I wasn't really allowed to do that, (the cat always managed to get up a tree and into safety however), and then back home for lunch. As they have got older, I don't see them quite as often, but Lilly, well we just fell in love with each other, a platonic kind of love which still exists today even though Lilly too has become an old lady, and… well…. I suppose I'm not so young myself nowadays.

But they were and still are my extended family, and that doesn't just include Lilly, Bella and Chestnut, but also their owners, Tommaso and Paula who I am very fond of and who have been very good to me. They are like my second mum and dad, as I woo, woo, woof at Ami and Francesco, I do the same to them at their house.

Let me tell you about the day I was in such a dilemma that I just didn't know what to do.

Ami and I were on our usual little walk which as always I really enjoyed and we were on our way home. Just before turning left onto the road which takes us to our house, Ami put my lead on as she always did, it is much safer for everybody if a dog is on a lead when on a road, but instead of walking on round the corner to go home I came to a halt, stood as still as a rock, and refused to continue. Ami looked at me wondering what the matter was and coaxed me to walk on home. But I was NOT going home…. She tried again, but no, I wanted to stay right there at that spot and wait. There was nothing she could do, so she just stood with me totally perplexed for a moment but then let go of my lead saying that she had to go home and if I didn't want to come, I could stay there. I didn't move, Ami walked a few metres along the road, realized that I was still not moving, so returned to where I was. She had obviously thought that she couldn't leave me alone on the lane.

Suddenly, it all became clear to her as Tommaso appeared from round the corner coming towards us in his car. I was so happy and wagged my tail at him when he stopped to say "hello". You see I had heard his car tooting at the bends when it was probably 1 km away and had recognized the sound, the one belonging to Tommaso's car, but Ami wouldn't have heard it. We dogs have got very, very good hearing, much better than you humans.

Ami and Tommaso exchanged a few words and then he was on his way in the opposite direction to the one we were going. All of a sudden, I just didn't know which way to go, should I follow Tommaso and go to his home for a while or continue with Ami to my home? What a difficult decision to make and it took me a few moments humming and harring but in the end I went with Ami after she explained to me that once we were home, I could go to Tommaso's house, if I wanted.

Learning the rules

I live in a big country house which is actually divided into two apartments, one is on the ground floor and the other one directly above it on the first floor. I live on the ground floor flat, the other one is used for our family and friends when they come to visit. When that happens, I'm not allowed to bark and I'm certainly not allowed to go into this holiday home, but when Ami is doing the cleaning before our guests are due to arrive, I sometimes sneak in to have a look around.

"What another lovely house I've got!" I think to myself as I wander out onto the large, sunny terrace to see if we have any other guests staying with us behind the plant pots, known as lizards. I chase them, but they are so quick, they always get away!!

We have a huge garden which has no fences around it and just continues to the neighbours' gardens, I have no idea where my garden ends and the neighbours' gardens begin so I expect half of the time I'm on their land rather than on my own. However, it doesn't usually seem to matter and the neighbours' dogs also wander around my garden probably not realizing it isn't theirs, so it's all give and take, isn't it? Most dogs, including me, are very protective of their territory and will bark when there is an intruder. This is to alert their owner. But it can be a bit confusing for us when we don't understand what garden is ours and what garden belongs to somebody else. In fact, sometimes I hear the little dogs that live up the lane in my garden barking at Ami, who then tells them to be quiet as she is actually in HER garden and not theirs, so they have no right to bark at her. They skuttle off all grumpily.

When I was little I used to be quite naughty and go wandering off to see my golden Labrador friend who lived down the hill a bit. You didn't have to go on any road to get there, just through gardens so it wasn't really dangerous. I really enjoyed this little adventure and started going every day, even though I knew Ami and Francesco were not happy with me when I returned.

-Where have you been, you little rascal? - they would say. -You must stay at home!! - they implored.

But I just couldn't help myself. Off I would go in the afternoon unnoticed to see my new friend. We got on so well together and just loved playing in his garden. I even met his family, who were very nice but seemed concerned about who I was and where I had come from. After all, I was still only a puppy and so as they say: -All good things come to an end!

One day while we were having a good play of tig in the garden, I saw Ami walking towards their gate. She didn't greet me or look pleased to see me with her usual warm smile and in fact straight away I found out she had come to take me home. I didn't want to go, and my friend didn't want me to go either. We looked into each other's eyes as I struggled to free myself from Ami's grasp. He gave a little yelp and cry, but to no avail. I was being taken home; our secret meetings were over.

The family had telephoned Ami to let her know of my frequent visits, and that they were a little worried about me wandering around alone. Amy and Francesco were worried too, so I had to be made to stay at home. What happened? The following afternoon, instead of being totally free to run wherever I wanted, I was put on a long lead in the garden just in front of the house. Amy explained to me that she was worried about me going on a road and getting hurt by a car or motor scooter. So,

36

although I endured being restricted that afternoon, I didn't enjoy it at all and decided it was better to be obedient and do as I was told. I didn't go to see my Labrador friend again.

Being taught or trained is very important but like with little children it takes time and a lot of patience. How many times has a child been at my house, and they touch my tail so the parents tell them not to do it. Then they do it again and again, and it's really bothering me because it hurts. I know, however, that if I give them a warning snarl or growl, it'll be me who gets into trouble.

Well, for us with four legs, it's also very important to learn and understand what we can and can't do and all of this starts from a very young age. I remember being a puppy and realizing I had to do a wee on the grass in the garden, not on the carpet in the house. Little babies have nappies because like us they can't control themselves and wet themselves. We, too wet ourselves especially when we are really happy or get excited, all of a sudden there is a little puddle of water on the floor and the next minute we are slipping and sliding in it.

This also happened with me when I was a little pup, but I remember that I was often carried outside and told to do a wee.

Other things I remember learning when I was a little puppy were to sit and stay, and to hold my paw up when I wanted some food. Of course, I didn't learn straight away, I was sometimes distracted by other things or I forgot or just couldn't be bothered, but because Amy and Francesco persisted I eventually got the message.

In actual fact, I'm very proud to mention that I got the message in two languages, I am a bilingual dog and understand commands in English and Italian. One of Amy's Italian friends once wanted me to go to her house to teach her dog English!!! What about that!!

Then of course another fundamental thing to learn is walking on the lead in an orderly fashion, not pulling or

going from one side to the other tripping up your owner. Today, even the country lanes near our house are quite busy with cars, motorbikes and scooters so this is really important, just being allowed to walk wherever you want could cause a nasty accident.

Like humans we dogs never stop learning, well, I suppose not until we get old, the saying does go: "You can't teach an old dog new tricks", doesn't it? But when we are young we have a capability that is unlimited.

You only have to think about the dogs that work in the Police Force. Amy and Francesco were speaking about them the other day after they had seen a police officer with his working dog at the Capodichino Airport in Naples. They had gone to pick Victoria up, and while waiting for her to come through arrivals, went to the café for a cappuccino. It was obviously coffee time for the police officer who worked at the airport too, as he came into the bar with his working companion, a German Shepherd dog, that was told to lie down and wait while he had his coffee. The dog obviously did so without hesitation and looked so beautiful and smart with his special police harness on that he got a lot of attention from the people in the cafe, including Amy and Francesco who took a photo of him to show me.

Then, there are the rescue dogs who find people under the rubble after an earthquake or buried deep in the snow after an avalanche. They too, are very smart!!! How do they do it? I don't really know because I have difficulty finding my bone in the garden! But the answer to that question is that they have been taught. If we dogs are not instructed, we cannot learn and only go on instinct.

Unfortunately, this can lead to dogs getting into trouble and not having a very pleasant life and the very sad thing is that sometimes it's not their fault but simply due to the fact that they have never been trained.

My Nana

Quite early on in my life I met another person who seemed to become part of the family for a period of time, a person who usually arrived in the evening with a big suitcase with strange smells on it. She was very nice and made a fuss of me, stroking me, rubbing my chest and talking to me, so straight away I decided that I liked her very much. I found out her name was Nana.

-Say hello to Nana! - Ami would say to me in the morning when Nana came into the kitchen for breakfast. She was also Victoria's Nana, but Ami's mum.

I wasn't really allowed to go into her bedroom much, in fact the door was usually tightly shut, but this didn't mean that Nana didn't want anything to do with me. On the contrary, in the after-noon when Amy was working in the study, she would look after me a bit, take me for a little walk, play rag or ball with me, and if I sat for a long time in front of the cupboard where my food was kept, she would also offer me biscuits. Yes, she was certainly very welcome to live with us.

Unfortunately, though, she obviously couldn't stay with us forever and had to go back to her own home which was far away. I could sense sadness in the air when she was due to return. The big suitcase was brought into the house from the storeroom, and things started to be put in it, Nana's clothes obviously, (not all of them though, some were left in the wardrobe of her room for later visits), and other things such as lemons, tomatoes or kiwis from the garden depending on the season, dried oregano and fennel seeds, chamomile tea and finally the ones with the most delicious smell of all, Italian chocolates. Of course, even though I sat in front of the suitcase with my paw up saying, *"Please!"*, I was never given one, they were presents to be taken to Nana's house, but in any case, chocolates are very bad for us doggies and should never be given to us.

The time had come for the big suitcase, packed and closed, to be wheeled out of the house and into the boot of the car. Nana would quickly say goodbye to me and then get into the car with Ami and Francesco to be driven away.

"I wonder when I'll see her again", I used to think sadly.

After one of Nana's first visits when I was a puppy, I was in her room just having a look and a sniff around, when I

found her slippers left on the floor.

"These smell nice", I thought. *"I think I'll take one to play with"*. I loved it! I could shake it, carry it into the garden and chew it. It had such a good taste! Sometime later though, when somebody nice came to visit and I fetched it to show it to them, Ami was not very happy and took it off me. She said it was dangerous for me, while I was chewing

it, I could swallow small parts of it which would give me a very nasty stomachache. She got my ball and played ball with me for a bit, but I really wanted Nana's slipper.

Next time Ami and Francesco went out they came home with a present for me. It was a rubber bone for me to chew and play with to replace the slipper. It was just the job and as it had been made especially for dogs, it was safe for me.

Fortunately, Nana used to come quite often which was really super as while she was staying with us, we would do special things together. For example, we would go to different places for a walk, so lots of interesting new smells to deal with, or to a café for a coffee, or a bar for an aperitif. These latter two not really very enjoyable for me because I just had to lie on the cold floor waiting for them to finish, but something which I really loved a lot was going to the beach in the evening to eat a pizza, lots of tasty cheesy bits for me too!

For quite a while now Nana hasn't been, probably since the time humans were wearing those coverings on their faces, the pandemic they call it, I think. I've missed having her company on a summer's afternoon while Ami is teaching. Sometimes I used to help Nana clean up the little path that leads you to Victor's steps in the garden. Nana would bend down and pull out all the invading grass getting her hands dirty and having a few problems with her knees, while I would find somewhere comfortable, either in a sunny spot or in a shady spot depending on the temperature and lie down to watch her.

Oh, maybe if there was a lizard to catch, I would get up and run after it. I never actually ever caught any, but it was good fun watching them run for their lives up the trunk of a tree.

I would also have a good bark and frighten Nana to death, should any other living creature, doggies or humans come near the garden.

-Stop barking! - she would firmly say to me.

Of course, I shared my Nana with Lilly too, as you can see in the picture below.

Yes, I really miss her and hope that she will come again soon to stay with us with the big suitcase with mysterious, far away smells on it. Or perhaps I could get a passport and go to visit her!

It is possible you know these days; I know of a few dogs who go on an aeroplane to visit family or go on a holiday.

My Toys

Like little children, we doggies especially when we are puppies love to play, and if possible, have toys to play with. I remember my first toy was a rag, which was just a piece of material that I could get a grip of with my teeth and play tug of war with the person who was holding the other end. I loved this game and as I shook the rag from  side to side, I snarled and growled at my opponent to show how big, strong and fierce I could pretend to be. If I was able to free the rag from the other person's grip and run off with it, I had won the game, and if I had been playing with Ami, she would give me a little applause and a well done.

When I was a little bigger and I was getting my adult teeth, Ami and Francesco bought me a special kind of rubber bone which I could chew on. That really helped my teething problems, but I also played run and fetch with it. Somebody threw it and I ran and fetched it back. That was good fun for a short time, but a bit tiring after a while, all this running backwards and forwards.

Then of course every now and again I was given a real bone when Ami or Francesco had been to the butcher's. Some people say they are an excellent option for keeping your dog's teeth and gums healthy and remove tartar from them, and let's say I preferred to chew on a bone for a while instead of having my teeth cleaned with a toothbrush. However, I didn't always fancy a bone, and sometimes, no sooner had someone given it to me, I would pick it up and take it to a secret place in the garden to bury it.

On one occasion that was just round the corner from the patio under the lemon tree because I didn't want to have to go far with this heavy bone in my mouth. So, I put it on the ground, and using my front feet dug what I thought was a deep hole, pushed the bone into it using my nose, and again with my nose pushed the soil on top of it. I was very pleased with myself! What an excellent job I'd done! Nobody will ever find it except me, and I will be so grateful to have it on a rainy day. Off I trotted, head held up high and tail up, to have a rest on the grass in the sunshine after all this hard work.

I was just drifting off when suddenly I heard a noise coming from where the lemon tree is and then saw Chestnut run past heading home with something in her mouth. Ami was standing there and said to me:

-You'll have to dig a bigger hole next time Tyson, as soon as you'd finished Chestnut appeared, sniffed around, found where your bone was straight away, moved the bit of soil that you'd covered it up with, and now has taken it home! I witnessed everything from Victoria's bedroom window!-

I couldn't believe it! I thought I had done everything so well.

"Oh well, I'll have to try harder next time", I thought to myself as I looked up to Ami. *"I probably wouldn't have remembered where I'd buried it anyway"*.

I rested my head on the grass and closed my eyes ready to have a nap.

While we are on the subject of burying things, I'd just like to point out that I am a very much, "waste not want not dog!" What does this expression mean exactly? Well, it means if you never waste anything you will always have what you need. Therefore, if I'm given macaroni for my dinner and I can't manage it all, I take one at a time out into the garden to bury it for a rainy day. I suppose the problem is again if I re-

member where I bury it.

Getting back to toys, the photo below shows me playing with Victoria's teddy, which I wasn't really allowed to.

Like Nana's slipper, they are not really safe for us as we could swallow a small part. You can actually tell from my face I was being a bit naughty. But I was saying, *"Oh, go on, don't be a spoil sport. Let's have a game with this old teddy!"*.

Well, once I took it into the garden and buried it. Again, I wanted to keep it for a rainy day, when I had nothing to do, I could dig it up and play with it, but would you believe I never found it? I expect one day when Francesco or Ami are doing the garden, they will come across it and I might even get into trouble. It's a good job it wasn't Victoria's Winnie the Pooh who was perched on a shelf in her bedroom and who I desperately wanted to get hold of. If only I could get him down to play with him. But I was never allowed to touch him. He was Victoria's and still is.

Another favourite game of mine was football with the two boys who lived near Lilly. The ball was bigger than me but it was still a great game. Lilly sometimes joined in as well, but I was much better than she was! She was older than me but was a short-legged dog, so had a problem getting hold of the ball. I was only a puppy so also had short legs, but I hoped one day they would get longer, which they did.

At my home though, I came across another kind of ball which Ami took with her when she went to play tennis. They were much easier for me to cope with, and Ami gave me one to call my own. She and I played a new game with this ball and it taught me to count to three. Ami threw the ball against the outside wall of the house and caught it. If I could, I was allowed to catch it too, but usually she got it. Ami did this three times and when she said number three, it was for me to catch. Sometimes I did a little jump into the air and caught it straight away, other times I didn't and so had to chase the ball down the drive but eventually got it and brought it back.

When I wasn't playing with my toys, they were put in my toy drawer just near the front door of the house. I soon learned and remembered that my rag and chewy bone and now my ball were kept there, so when I fancied a play in the evening I sat in front of the drawer and poked it until I got attention from someone who then played with me for ten minutes.

In the summer, there was yet another new toy for me to play tug of war with and this one was called a rope. I would also like to just mention that I learnt the names of all my toys in both languages Italian and English. I had lots of fun with my new rope, but not only with my family, when Ami's little students came to do their English lesson, they couldn't wait to get into the garden and play "rope" with me.

Hen pecked

When a man talks about being hen pecked, he doesn't mean it literally, that a hen comes up to him and starts pecking at his toes. He means that his wife, girlfriend or partner goes on at him continually, criticizing his actions or behaviour or pulling him down for example.

I have been hen pecked, but not in this sense. In the literal one! Ami and Francesco have hens and a cockerel, the hens don't have any names, but the cockerel is called Pasqualino. Ami often calls out to him and he, together with his brood, all come running to the gate of their house either wanting some fresh leaves to eat or to be let out for a wander and a peck around the garden. And when I say peck, I mean peck!!! When I was a little pup, they pecked me! Not so much Pasqualini, but mainly the hens. They would gradually approach me, surround me and then peck, peck, peck!! On my back, or  near my ears, I was terrified and didn't know what to do. Fortunately, Ami and Francesco were always around and came to my rescue, shooing them away.

-Bark at them! - they told me, but I was only little, I only had my baby teeth, and they were taller and fatter than me at that time.

Now I'm bigger than they are, but unfortunately a dislikeness towards them has grown over the years. I really would like to get my own back, chase them around the garden, catch them and pin them down to the ground. But Ami and Francesco have ordered me not to touch them even when they are running free in the garden, I know that I can't grab one of them by the neck, I would love too but I have to content myself with a little run at them and a bark, and even then of course I get told off. My natural dog instinct would be to attack them, but I have been taught that that is wrong!

The last couple of years we have also had little chicks. Sometimes, a hen gets broody and Francesco puts some eggs under her and eventually little chicks hatch out. They are even more appetizing than the hens I can tell you, but again, dare I touch them!!!

When they get bigger they are allowed in the chicken house, which has an enclosed outside area so they can peck around in the fresh air. Some are never happy though, are they? There are two at the moment that are totally unappreciative of what they have, and everyday have to squeeze themselves out through a gap in the fence and explore the unprotected wide world. Surely that gives me the right to chase them, doesn't it? Absolutely not!

-Don't you dare touch them! - Ami warns me, then.

-Leave them alone now! - Francesco says firmly.

Good job Victoria's in London or she would have some reprimand to give me too.

As I stand behind them watching them while they are freely enjoying pecking the ground, completely oblivious to my presence, let alone fearful, I'm imagining all sorts of things, all of which, however, have to stay in my imagination.

Still, I have learnt to make myself very useful, and am very proud of myself. As daytime is ending and it's getting dusk, Francesco and I have to make sure the little chicks have gone inside their house, and we close the wooden gate so they are safe for the night. With those two mischievous chicks being out of the enclosure, it is my job to lead them to the fence and encourage them through the gap so they too can enter the house and roost for the night. I feel I've become such a clever boy. Do you realize I've mastered the skills of a sheep dog?? I wander if I could enter a competition like Ami's cousin's dog does. He is a proper sheep dog and works with sheep.

The other job I love assisting with is when Francesco has to cut Pasqualino's claws. You remember he's the cockerel, right? Well, first of all we have to catch him, Francesco's just about to grab him when I bark with the excitement and Pasqualino runs away. I get a bit of a telling off about that, so keep quiet to make sure Francesco is able to pick him up the second time and then he holds him firmly under his arm and trims his kind of thumb nail with a special pair of scissors. It's a little tricky you know

because cockerels can be quite ferocious sometimes, so we're risking our lives doing this little job.

I love doing these important tasks with Francesco, and I'm now such a help, I don't know how he would manage without me, really!!

Cleaning day

You know puppies love to play, they are full of bounce, curiosity, playfulness and energy, and that included me too. I loved picking things up off the floor and running into the garden with them, mainly Francesco's socks, but other small things too, even underwear... and it was even more fun when Ami was loading the washing machine and sometimes dropped some small item on the floor. I would get hold of it and gallop into the garden with it, Ami running after me telling me to drop it.

I would be on the scene too when there were other household jobs to do. My aim was to make Ami's garden jobs into games to make the work lighter and more fun for her. On a nice, dry sunny morning when Ami started brushing up the leaves on the drive, I would be running and playing there too, getting in the way and trying to bite the brush, growling at it as if it was some ferocious animal. How brave I was! Ami would tell me to get out of the way and leave the brush alone otherwise I might get hurt, and I did actually get clonked accidentally every now and then, but it didn't put me off playing and I'm sure Ami was really enjoying the game too.

Another time when we had lots of fun was when Ami was cleaning the furniture with the duster. I just loved that game which was a bit like tug of war with my rag. As she was dusting the furniture, I would try to get hold of it and then run into the garden with it waiting for Ami to come and chase me, which she did.

But to top it all was the feather duster, I just loved that to bits and as it was a bit bigger, it was easier for me to grab it off Ami, so I usually won that game. Then of course I would race into the garden with it and as Ami came after me to get it back, I would run off with it to the other side of the cicas plant. What a great game that was!! I'm sure Ami preferred playing with me instead of doing all this housework! Surely it could all wait.

The clean and smelly dog

We dogs like to be clean too, you know. We often lick our legs and feet and other parts to give them a wash. And we like to make our bed and maybe shake it a little to get rid of a bit of dust and hair. Yes, that is a bit of a problem, our hair which falls off us in the house, especially at certain times of the year when we moult, that is getting our summer coat. Giving us a brush can help tackle the problem, and it is so relaxing, I just love it!

Then some of us like certain smells to use as a kind of perfume. We sniff the ground, find this lovely smell and sort of rub our neck or shoulder in it. The only problem is, it is not at all pleasant to you humans, as I experienced one day.

My friend Lilly often puts perfume on, and then I notice that Ami tells her quite strictly to go out of the house. The next day I notice she smells of roses or other flowers and she's all nice and silky.

-Lilly's had a bath! - I hear Ami say. Anyway, I don't know what got a hold of me the other day, but I just could not resist it, well you human men put aftershave on, don't you? And it was all well planned too because Ami and Francesco had guests, so just right for me to have my lovely scent on, no? No!

As they were sitting around the table in the garden and I wanted to join them, I got told quite briskly to move away.

"What have I done?", I thought to myself, looking intensely at Ami to see if I could understand why she was all of a sudden so angry with me. I tried again to get near them, but the same thing happened, Ami was angry, Francesco was angry, and the guests looked disgustingly at me telling me to back off. I just didn't get it, but decided it was better for me to lie away from them to avoid getting shouted at again. I'm a very sensitive boy and my feelings get hurt very easily and while they continued to talk, laugh and drink their coffee, I stared the whole time at Ami, trying to figure out why she was behaving so nastily to me. What on earth had I done?

Eventually the guests left, and we were alone.

-You smelly boy! - Ami said to me, then sniffed me and went *urghhhh*. She repeated this several times and I got the message.

I was a smelly boy, a nice smell for me, but obviously not for you humans as the smell was similar to when you fertilize the garden. Ami was getting bowls out and water and my Trixie shampoo. It was bath time.

Me and water

I don't really like water, except to drink. I've been given a bath quite a few times and don't really care for it, if I can get out of the bowl and escape, I will do. But on this occasion, after having already been in trouble all morning, I thought I had better do as I was told, and Ami had anyway warned me not to put a foot out of the bath. Actually, I quite enjoyed it, but the best part was when I was allowed out and I could go racing round the garden to get dry. Awesome. And I haven't put any more perfume on since.

It's the same thing when I've been taken to the beach. I don't really care for getting my paws wet, and for actually having a swim, well, I think I may have done this just once in my life.

Would you believe on the 31st of December Ami went swimming in the sea and was inviting me in too? Was she mad or not on the last day of the year going into the freezing sea? I don't know! I did get a little bit wet, just to make her happy.

The other day I got shown photos of Tommy, Ami's cousin's dog who apparently has a swim with his owner Linda.

-And this is the English Channel, not the warm Mediterranean Sea where you live! - I got told. So maybe the next time they take me to the beach I'll try to make more of an effort. I think I take after Nana because she is not too keen on water either.

The Uninvited Friend

It was a lovely sunny afternoon and as usual I waited for Amy to get ready to take me on my walk. It's the best activity of the day to go for a walk, well apart from eating that is, stopping to smell every lamp post to understand who has been there, seeing different things and sometimes having a little adventure with another dog. Sometimes the dogs I meet are friendly, so we sniff each other, wag our tails and carry on, but other times I've experienced ones that would have liked to have eaten me alive.

They're much bigger than me and a lot stronger of course, to the extent that even their owners have problems controlling them on their lead. They pull hard to get near me, snarl and growl and show their fully grown teeth, the hair on their back is raised to show how angry they are, and I, what do I do? Well, I stand tall and growl or bark at them and show them my set of teeth without fully grown canines. They're those long, pointed ones which you use to attack with, but mine haven't grown properly and have remained little. In any case, I try to put up a good fight getting the hair along my spine to stand up on end, even though I'm so scared I could ....in my pants.

"Good job Amy's with me", I think to myself. *"She'll protect me"*, and she always does as we walk out of that terrifying situation. When we're completely out of danger, I feel so relieved, you can't imagine, and I run and jump with joy, after going through those frightening life-threatening moments. I look at Amy and say in my head, *"That was a close one, wasn't it??? Didn't I do well, I was so brave!!!"*. And we continue on our lovely walk, just she and I.

On this particular day, this didn't happen though! We had just got round the corner where all the interesting smells started when this medium-sized dog crawled under a big, heavy, iron gate to get out. He wagged his tail to say "hello", and proceeded to come with us, on our walk. I was not at all happy with his decision, and first of all growled at him. Then, when he continued not to realize that he wasn't welcome, I snapped at him. Nothing! He followed us quite happily, oblivious to my warnings. In fact, I was not enjoying my outing at all, with this dirty, messy, smelly tramp of a dog with long, straggly hair all over his face covering his eyes with us. How could he see where he was going? And wherever I went he was always there, right behind me. My patience was growing very thin!

Amy tried telling him to go home, but he was insistent on having a walk together with us. She was probably worried that he may get lost, but in the end, she gave up and said no more to him. Then, she turned to me!!! Was I going to get a telling off about all of this? Surely not. It wasn't my fault!!! I didn't, but simply got an explanation of this poor dog often being alone and probably just wanting some company for a walk.

Apparently, not all dogs have really devoted owners like me, who make sure a walk is fitted into their busy daily schedule; some dogs are just left alone all day, either inside or out, while their humans are at work, or busy doing other things. Day after day after day, they can become extremely lonely and bored and so these poor canines like to tag onto other people, pretending that they too are getting that precious attention that they have never known.

"How sad!", I thought and then proceeded on my way deciding to tolerate the newcomer. He was, in fact, no problem at all and at one point just seemed to disappear.

However, it did become quite a regular thing, but I just learnt to accept it, and really, deep down, felt sorry for the old boy. He was so unkempt, as I said before he had all this long hair in front of his eyes, but on his body you could see that his fur was all tangled and knotted. He really did need some attention, a nice bath and groom or if the tangles wouldn't come out, a good haircut. The ironic thing was that his owner was apparently a hairdresser!!!! Only for humans though!

Really though, if you choose to have a dog, these jobs are important because neglecting them can lead to other problems which can cause the dog to suffer, or which can be a risk to humans. I hope that one day I will meet our uninvited friend and he will be all spruced up, with a handsome haircut so I can see his eyes and have a healthy, shiny coat, groomed and in order. I'm sure he could be quite handsome, not as much as me, of course!

The dog with no name

This leads me to another very sad story. The story of Pluto, well, Ami gave him the name of Pluto, but really he was the dog with no name.

I have a cousin dog called Stella, that lives up our lane. We don't particularly get on that well, in fact she really infuriates me when she comes galloping at high speed all over my garden looking for lizards and she petrifies poor Lilly when we have to pass her house on our walk, and as a matter of fact me too really.

I also sense that Ami is nervous of her because Stella will sometimes growl very deeply at her for no reason. Ami knows that you mustn't show any fear towards a dog because they will sense it, but she says she just can't help it.

Anyway, when Stella was young another dog came to play with her who had a home but didn't seem to want to live there. The owner of this dog didn't seem to care about him too much, consequently Pluto, as Ami had named him, got up to terrible mischief and eventually had to be taken away to a doggy home.

Why did he get into so much trouble? Because he hadn't been trained and hadn't been taught what was right and what was wrong. Do you remember what we spoke about in chapter 5 Learning the rules? This is an example of why it is so important.

Living with a teenager

When there are teenagers in the family there's always a lot going on. Of course, they go to school in the morning, then return home, homework in the afternoon, maybe some sport activities in the evening or spend some time hanging out with their friends, and in some cases, they also have a part-time job. This was the case for Victoria, alongside studying at a college for hairdressing, she also worked in a salon. So, there were comings and goings galore. Victoria had her own little moped so usually was able to take herself wherever she was going, but on a rainy day Ami would accompany her by car.

And that was only during the week! When the weekend came, movement increased. First of all, there were numerous fashion parades from Victoria's bedroom to the big mirror situated in the hall by the front door where Victoria would examine in great detail what she had on and study her hair and make-up. The front door was usually opened to allow in more light to enable her to see better, so it was impossible for me to have a quiet lie down on the comfy  mat there, I was always in the way, and it was too cold and draughty. Victoria sometimes asked for advice from her mum, and also from me.

-Which looks better on me, Tyson? - she would enquire, and I'd look her up and down thinking that she looked awesome in anything. Then, when eventually an outfit had been decided on, lots of perfume was sprayed everywhere which was lovely but it made me sneeze a bit. At last, she was ready.

All very exciting really but talk about trying to get a good night's sleep on a Saturday... Victoria would go out way past my bedtime, then Francesco would go to work early in the morning, before my natural waking up time. Not long after Victoria would return home from her night clubbing by the sea, and her early morning breakfast with friends, so you can imagine after such an interrupted night I would be pretty weary on Sunday.

However, it was to all come to an end shortly after Victoria's twentieth birthday. There was a mixture of excitement, worry, happiness and sadness in the air, and on the 3rd of November Victoria wheeled a very large suitcase out of the house to be put into the car and off she went with her parents, not to return for some time. I mean, I was used to her going on holidays, and after a week the house would again be full of her laughter, jokes, perfume and her belongings left here and there all over the house, but this time she did not return after a week, or even a month, or even 2 months.

"When am I going to see her again?", I thought to myself as I looked at Ami, who was carrying on with her usual chores, but I could tell that she too was missing her daughter immensely.

In fact, this is a poem that Ami wrote for Victoria:

I've written a few lines just to say
What it'll be like when you're away
After midnight sandwiches,
no breadcrumbs on the side
And outside a motor scooter for me to ride,
To replace an untidy, messy room
My sad face and a heart full of gloom.

How will I be able to listen to those nightclub songs
Without an empty feeling, because to you they belong
Together we were when we listened to them
The times you went dancing again and again
I'll put a smile on my face
and think how lucky I've been
Another girl like you, has anyone ever seen?

A lot we've been through in this life
And who knows what more before you come a wife.
There's plenty of time for that, you so often say.
You're right and like Nana says
sensible in so many ways.

How proud we are of the young lady you've become
At one time you were little like our puppy Tyson.
But now you're all dressed up and ready to go out,
And I can really say, there's absolutely no doubt
How lovely you look, so elegant and smart.
Whose comments will you ask for when we're apart?

After you've left,
your perfume drifts through the house,
It won't be there; I'll have to do without
So many wonderful things
like your happy smiling face,
your contagious laughter

And that warm and loving embrace.

Our intimate chats and pieces of advice
To have a daughter is really so nice.
But soon she must go and live her life
A little bit sad, but oh so right.
To explore, experience and new things find.
It's all so good to widen the mind.

But I just want you to know this,
When we say cheerio with a kiss
Always in my thoughts you will be
Until the time comes for us to see
Each other again, ready to share
The things we've done and the new clothes we wear.

The little girl you were once I've forgotten never,
Our precious life up to now always together
May this love between us last forever and ever.

So, what can I say? This was a new chapter in everyone's life, nothing would ever be quite the same again, but Victoria was fulfilling her dream to become a hairdresser in London, she was happy and excited, and we all knew the opportunities that the future could offer her in London were unlimited. Therefore, we all had to get used to this new routine of comings and goings from the big, capital city.

Not only this, though. We also had to become accustomed to Victoria's new hairstyles. The first time she returned home for a holiday her hair was short, straight and green, then another time blue, purple, blonde, red, black, short and straight or long and curly.

Then once she had had plaited extensions put in that came down to her waist.

"My goodness", I thought, *"is it really her?"*

The funny thing is that after about three days Victoria could no

longer stand the weight of this extra hair on her head, and she and Ami spent hours sitting in the lounge taking them out. It was all in a heap on the floor as if a black sheep had been sheared.

And guess who had the idea of making me into a black, curly haired sheep dog? Ami! And here I am!

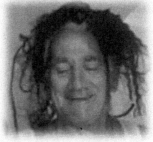

I wasn't the only one who had to suffer. Francesco was dressed up too!

All this has taught me that when Victoria is due to return home for a visit, I never know quite what she is going to look like.

It's no problem however, I'm always happy to see her and love all the fuss she gives me, well the stroking and rubbing my chest part yes, but I'm not really too keen on all the picking up she likes to do. I'm getting a bit old for all that though I put up with it because I know her visit isn't very long.

Lilly loves the extra attention too which I get a bit jealous of, but I know Victoria loves me more.

She often says that one day she'll take me back to London with her. Ami says that I wouldn't like it at all living in an apartment in a city. Who knows?

A different Christmas

I'd like to tell you about the Christmas of 2019, that was so different from other Christmases.

Usually, I start to see a movement of things some days before Christmas, clothes are taken into the spare room and put on the bed, and sometimes there are nice smelly things there too like salamis or Parmesan cheese. Suitcases with strange smells on them are brought in from the storeroom and it is then when I realize what is about to happen. All the things on the bed get put into the cases and Amy and Francesco disappear for a length of time.

I don't really mind them going because I get to stay with Lilly and her family in her house, and so it is a kind of holiday for me too. Lilly's family are very kind to me letting me sleep indoors in front of the fire, the food is excellent and of course I can play with Lilly, Chestnut and Bella. So, it is great fun. Obviously, if I didn't have a place to go to it would be dreadful, a nightmare, I wouldn't have any food or warmth or company and would get terribly sad. I know Amy and Francesco go to see Lilly's owners before leaving to make sure it is ok for me to be there.

In 2019 it didn't happen! They didn't put any things into the spare room later to be packed into suitcases, and in fact they didn't go away, so I didn't have my holiday with Lilly and family!!! *"This is strange"*, I thought, even more so when on Christmas Eve all the furniture was moved in the living room to allow the table to be extended to seat lots of people and the rugs were rolled up and taken away into the study.

That, I DID NOT like at all!!!!! Where was I meant to lie down??? Still, there were a lot of good smells coming from the kitchen and every so often Francesco dropped something on the floor, so I suppose this compensated for the upheaval of the living room.

I didn't realize what a lovely surprise I was in for, though!!! It was late afternoon, and I was just getting ready to have a nice snooze in my house when all of a sudden Amy and Francesco went out in the car. They weren't too long and guess who was with them when they returned????? Victoria from London, with all those now familiar city smells .... I was SO happy!!!! She made a big fuss of me and played ball and rag and hide and seek and even nursed me when I wanted a little nap. It was wonderful, the family was complete!!!

Well, not really, because the day after other members of the family arrived to have a special lunch with us, one that goes on and on with lots of good titbits for us dogs too. There were people everywhere, in the garden because the weather was glorious, in the kitchen, sitting at the table in the living room and children playing on the floor in the hall. It wasn't a problem for me because Amy had put my house in a quiet spot if I wanted some peace, but actually I enjoyed playing ball in the garden and badminton with the children, though I got told off for running off with the shuttlecocks. Then evening came and they were all still at our house, I was exhausted so went into my house for a nap, there was no other place to go with no carpets down! Eventually, I heard no more voices, there was peace and the day had ended. It had been a very special Christmas Day!

The next day started quite normally, milk for breakfast, a walk around the garden, a play with Victoria and an early lunch … But then it turned into something that I had never experienced before. After lunch Francesco's nephew, Luigi took Victoria, Amy and I in the car to the town of Massa. We got out of the car and I'd never seen anything like it! So many people, children, pushchairs, prams and dogs!!!! What on earth were we going to do? Where were we going?

Victoria tied a kind of card around my neck with a big paw on it. I didn't find that very comfy, so she then put it on my lead and next thing we were off, on a walk but with a few thousand other people.

We were taking part in the traditional Italian Boxing Day "Marcialonga". A long, organized walk with tasty bites to eat on the way. Usually there is just Amy and me on a walk, in fact I was a little apprehensive and fretted when I couldn't see her even though I was with Victoria... I wanted the three of us to always be together, but with the crowds it was difficult, and there were a lot of other dogs too, of all kinds, big, enormous, small, old, young. Some of them had the card with the big paw on it around their neck, it was obviously not a new thing for them. They gave me a superior look which plainly said that they had done this before, it was not their first time like mine! In fact, I was a little nervous of overtaking some and only did it when Amy walked right next to me. She and Victoria seemed to be in quite a hurry and I too was fairly keen to get to the end, but when did it end? We walked uphill, round corners, over two bridges and eventually stopped to have a bite of sausage.

Then it was downhill, round more corners and down steps until I eventually recognized smells, we were getting near to where we had set off on this marathon.... Was I glad! I had walked 20 thousand steps according to Victoria's new Fitbit watch!!!! That was a record for me, so when we got home it was dinner and straight to bed..

The day after I was told to get into the car again. I was a bit reluctant and wondered if it was going to be a repeat of the day before, but it wasn't, it was just one of our usual strolls by the sea, so I was highly relieved. It was a great experience, but I don't want to repeat it until next Christmas.

A dog is a man's best friend

If you remember after going to my new home and meeting Ami for the first time, I made a promise to myself to love and protect my family until death do us part. This is what a dog does, it is probably the most loyal animal on earth, maybe together with a horse. I know this because my cousin Tommy, who lives in England, shares his owner with a horse, and so has learnt a lot about them.

You can see what a fine dog Tommy is in this photo: he had very, very long eyelashes when he was a pup, longer than Victoria's false ones in fact, but more importantly look at those lovely, sharp white canines! I could feel a little jealous because mine didn't finish growing and are only short, but never mind, we all have our own cross to bear, don't we?

Tulsa the horse is extremely handsome too. It is said that a horse will continue to walk, trot or run until its rider wants it to, even if the horse is absolutely exhausted, it will show loyalty right to the end.

Dogs are similar and I too can tell you about a time when I was suffering but didn't give up for the love of my human. It was a few years ago that I started to feel a bit off colour, some days were ok, but others I felt really ill to the point that I just rested in my bed. Ami was very kind to me, she looked me all over to try to understand what was wrong with me, had quiet discussions with Francesco and made sure I drank water and ate something. One day I would feel rotten, and then another day a little better and on one of these better days I decided to go and visit Lilly. All was good until after a little nap at her house, I found I couldn't get up and walk. I struggled but no way were my back legs able to support me. Fortunately, Tommaso noticed this and telephoned Francesco and Ami. Francesco came to fetch me, carried me home, and later that morning he and Ami took me to the vet.

I really hate going there, it makes me shake all over when they put me on that cold, stainless steel examining table, but Filippo the vet is very nice and always makes a fuss of me before looking me over. He gave me a general check up and said I had a problem with my hip joints, so I had to take some medicine.

I recovered quite quickly after taking my medicine, which I didn't like at all needless to say. In fact, each time I had to take a pill, I managed to spit it out several times until eventually Ami wrapped it up in a nice, tasty slice of ham and then it went straight down the red lane.

Life returned to normal for a while, but then during the hot summer I started to feel unwell again. This time, however, there weren't really any signs. My legs were ok, and so in the coolness of the evening Ami would take me on our usual short stroll, but I found it hard to keep up with her even though she was not rushing. She would stop and wait for me and stroke me and probably thought it was the heat, even though like I said we were walking in the evening, not in the hot afternoon. Of course, you must never forget that in very hot weather the pavements heat up and burn our pads, so we should never be taken on our walkies in those conditions. Have you ever tried to walk barefoot on a stoney beach in soaring temperatures? It burns the bottoms of your feet, and you have to rush into the sea to cool them off. Well, it's the same for us, only there is usually no water to walk into to cool our pads down.

Anyway, what was I saying? Oh yes, about not being able to keep up with Ami on my walk and she thought it was due to the heat. Would you believe a little later on in the week Ami's cousin Ellen came for a holiday and her husband thought it was because I was overweight, too fat!!! My body was too heavy for my thin legs to carry it around, especially up the hills. Thanks to him I noticed that my portions at breakfast and dinner were cut back!!! I had obviously been put on a diet. Thanks a lot, mate!!!! I had heard this word "diet" quite a lot in our house, somebody was usually on it, either Victoria or Francesco, or they were getting told off by Ami because they hadn't been on it. Now it was my turn.

Unfortunately, my problems didn't stop there. Ami noticed that my coat wasn't looking too good, I was scratching myself and the pads on my paws were very dry. Yet again, I had to endure another trip to the vet and this time they thought I was suffering from an allergy, consequently more pills. Still, I enjoyed spitting them out, and then getting lots of tasty tit bits to help them down, not a spoonful of sugar, like Mary Poppins said, but a juicy piece of chicken or steak, or some cheese.

While I was at the vets, shaking like a leaf on that cold, metal table, they decided I needed something else done too, and that was to give a blood sample. To go through this, I needed what Ami called, "a party hat", but it wasn't a hat that went on my head, I had to have it on my nose and when it was securely fastened, I couldn't open my mouth. It is basically a safeguard to prevent the dog from biting the vet if it suffers any pain or discomfort. Well, I certainly did when Filippo poked the needle into my leg to draw out some blood so they could examine it, and naturally went to bite him to make him stop, but of course due to the party hat, I couldn't open my mouth. It was quite infuriating and scary, but Francesco and Ami were near me, holding me, scratching my chest and talking to me gently and encouragingly to make it all as easy as possible for me.

After this not so pleasant experience, even Filippo stroked me and lifted me down from the table. He didn't want me to hate him because he'd hurt me with the needle, which had only hurt for an instance, and I'd already forgotten about it anyway. So, he put me safely on the floor and stroked me again, after all, what he had had to do was only for my benefit. I quite liked him anyway, you can really sense if a person is a doggie lover or not, and he was not only a doggie lover, but an animal lover in general. I remember when I was a very small pup, he came to my house to give me my first vaccinations. They are very important for us to have to protect us from getting nasty diseases, but even so I shook all over from the very end of my nose to the tip of my tail when he jabbed me. Again, he didn't just put me down and leave me,  but held me in his arms and gave me a cuddle and after a few seconds I licked his face all over and thought how much I liked him.

The devastating news

So, if you remember at the vets, they put a needle very gently into my leg to take some blood from my vein which was then put into a special container to be analysed. This is called a blood sample and the very clever analysts can understand lots and lots of things about your body by doing experiments with the blood.

Unfortunately for me the blood didn't tell a good story about my body, but the complete opposite. It showed that I was suffering from a very nasty illness called Leishmaniasis, which we dogs can get from a mosquito biting us.

When Francesco and Amy received this news from the vet, I could straight away feel great sadness in the air, Amy didn't smile much and Francesco stopped whistling and when Ami and I were on our little walk together I noticed that she stopped in front of the little chapel

that we go past to say a prayer, and as she was doing so, her eyes became wet. She knelt down to hug me and the water from her eyes dropped onto my nose. I licked it and thought how tasty it was, nice and salty, mmmm!

Later on, that evening Amy and Francesco were talking about the symptoms that I had had, the problems with my legs, muscle atrophy, with my coat, and I sometimes had a runny nose, and suffered from tiredness. These were all the symptoms of this illness and now it all made sense. I could feel that Ami was mortified about the fact she had thought I was slow because of being overweight, it had been proved that it had nothing to do with that, but it was this nasty illness.

The good news was that you can live with this disease providing that you take medicine to keep it at bay. And so that's what I had to do, and fortunately in quite a short time I started to feel much better.

Some time later, another trip to the vets and another sharp needle inserted in my leg to get the red stuff out proved that my body was fighting these naughty devils who had made me feel ill. I could stop taking one load of medicine but had to keep on taking a little pill every morning.

-Come on! - Ami would say to me -time for your pill, if not you'll get pregnant! - she joked.

Honestly!!! What was she talking about! I am a boy!!!

Needless to say, I didn't like it at all and got very good at spitting it out, unless it was hidden in something nice and tasty. Or sometimes it used to just stick to my gum and later would fall out on the carpet, then of course if Ami found it, I would get a telling off and was made to swallow it, (again in something tasty!). Well, it was saving my life!!!!! This has now gone on for years and I'm still here enjoying life, even though I know Ami has suffered tremendously thinking that I would not make it. Sometimes she looked at me with sad eyes and a breaking heart and whispered to me: -How could I live without you?-

Then one day she started to write about me. Therefore, if nothing else, this unpleasant experience has at least had one positive aspect, and that is inspiring Ami to write this book about me.

While we're being morbid, let me just tell you that we dogs also suffer a lot if our owners are unwell, or in fact go to heaven. We miss them, grieve for them and find it very hard to adapt to life without them.

This is what happened to my English friend Sky. His dad suddenly died, which was a great shock to him and all the family and feeling that maybe his mum needed some extra love, he followed her around all day. We dogs can sense a person's mood and want to help out as much as we can, and actually this gesture helped his mum get through this very sad time. You know, we are also taken to hospitals and care homes to comfort the elderly or poorly. Stroking us or having physical contact with us can be very beneficial to them and make them feel a little better.

Anyway, let's move on to something a little more cheerful!

My daily routine

When I hear the word "routine", it always reminds me of Ami's English lessons. She's a teacher you see, and I often hear her asking her pupils to tell her about their daily routine, what they do in the morning, the afternoon, the evening, or maybe at the weekend... and to do that correctly you have to use the Present Simple Tense. So, I've learnt a bit of English grammar too.

What about my routine then? What do I do every day? Well, I wake up at different times and the first thing I do is go to see if Ami or Francesco are awake. If Ami is up, she'll let me out into the garden so I can do a wee, have a sniff around to see who's been during the night, and sometimes a bark, but I have to be careful about barking because I'm not allowed to do so before 7am, it's too early and I disturb whoever is still asleep, Francesco usually. Sometimes though, if Ami is still tired and doesn't want to get up, I get told to go back to bed.

-Ninnananna! - she says.

That's "go to sleep" in Italian. And of course, I do what I'm told and go back into my bed, or latterly if nobody's around, I've been enjoying a little, early morning lie on the sofa. However, as soon as I hear footsteps from the bedroom, I have to jump off quickly and make out I was lying on the rug. Everybody believes I was, so no getting into trouble. What a clever boy I am!

When eventually Ami and Francesco do get up, they go to the kitchen to have breakfast, and guess what, me too. Ami shows me the milk bottle and asks me if I'd like some, to which I reply with one woof and wag my tail enthusiastically. Recently she's been telling me to give two woofs instead of just one to correspond to the two words "Yes, please". Well, sometimes I remember to do woof, woof and other times I don't and just wish she would hurry up and pour the milk into my dish. But this is only the beginning of the performance because following on to this I have to sit and say "please", which I do by raising my paw off the ground, (not too high though!), and then I must wait patiently sitting down while she pours the milk into my black dish and replaces the lid on the milk bottle. While all this is going on she says:

-Sit and stay,
until I say,
good boy,
enjoy!-

I am finally allowed to lap up my delicious milk, which I drink quietly and slowly without slopping any of it onto the floor. If by chance Lilly is visiting, she has hers outside as she splashes it everywhere and seems to get it onto her chin, which then drips onto the floor making a big mess.

That was all quite exhausting, so I am then ready for a nap on the kitchen mat while the humans have their breakfast.

Then what do I do? Well, Francesco is usually at home in the morning and normally does something quite exciting in the garden, so I accompany him. We go to make sure the chickens are ok, collect the eggs from the hen house, or Francesco does some gardening while I try to catch lizards.

I love being involved in all of this, but every so often pop back to the house to see what Ami is doing. I run in and put my nose to the ground to sniff where she is. Is she in the bathroom, or bedroom? I go running through and then see out of the corner of my eye that she's standing in the living room, and I had just run past her. When she gets dressed, I like to be there to see what clothes she's going to wear that day. They tell me a lot about her activities for the morning, if she's going to do lessons, do jobs in the house or gardening, or best of all, if she's going to take me for a walk!!! You see, they all have a particular smell on them that helps me understand her plans for the day.

I don't always predict correctly though. It has happened that she's got her walking clothes on but is doing a quick tidy-up in the lounge. I'm quite excited and waiting impatiently to go out, when all of a sudden, I hear her shout:

-Who's been on the sofa? Look at all this hair! What a mess!!-

I sit down, put my ears back and look at her apologetically wanting to say to her:

"Well, it was only for 5 minutes!".

She takes the cover off angrily and gives it a shake outside, puts it back, tells me not to dare go on the sofa again and off we go.

Another example of me not guessing Ami's plans for the morning is when she's wearing something that she usually does her lessons in but then tells me that she's going shopping and won't be long.

-Vado a fare la spesa - she says.

(Speaking to me in English and Italian ensures I will always be a bilingual dog!). I put my very sad and un-happy look on my face to try to persuade her not to go and leave me, but all to no avail, she gives me a stroke on the head and is off either in the car or on the motor scooter with Francesco.

In the summer Ami and Francesco often go to the beach. They make sure I have plenty of fresh water and again say that they won't be long. This expression "won't be long" is a bit unclear as it can mean between fifteen minutes and eight hours!

Of course, what I do depends very much on the climate. If it's very hot I like to plonk myself on the grass in the shade of the olive tree and have a nap and then I go into the sun and have another nap or to vary the routine a little I may go inside to have a nap on the comfy rug in the lounge or in the bedroom, and when I've sufficiently cooled off I go out in the sun again, yes, you've guessed it, to have another shut eye. It's hard work all this up and down and inside and out, and most of all making the decisions of where to go.

During cooler times of the year, I'm in the house more, either in my basket or on a mat somewhere, but as soon as I hear any noises outside, I like somebody to open the front door to let me out so I can go out and investigate. If Amy is doing a lesson in person or online I get into trouble if I do this more than once, disturbing her and making a noise outside. Even if she's not doing a lesson I get told off for wanting to go out all the time, because of course when I have dealt with the matter, I want to come in again. I'm a very clever boy because at a young age I learned not to scratch the solid wooden front door when I wanted to come in because my human parents taught me to do a little woof when I wanted the door opened. Well, it starts off as a little woof, but if nobody opens the door, I increase the volume and the number to show that I'm getting a bit fed up with waiting.

Sometimes, I go round to the kitchen door, which is glass, to peer in to see if anybody's there.

When Ami has finished doing her lessons, she obviously has free time to devote to me. Therefore, I stand in front of the cupboard where my biscuits are kept and wait to be offered some, and if I'm not, I  do a woof woof to edge her on, or I follow her everywhere around the house just to make sure she doesn't forget that I'm ready for my walk.

I'm a very lucky boy because I usually have a walk every day. Even though we have a very big garden and I'm free to wander around mine and the neighbours', I love to get out with Ami to have a good smell to see who's been around and what's been going on. Then of course I leave my calling card so all the local doggies know that I've been out and about. It's our way of socializing.

Our local walk is along the lane to the little chapel where the Madonnina is, and then up to the top of the hill from where you can see our village of S. Agata and in the distance the gulf of Salerno. We then walk downhill across a field where there is an amazing view of Capri on the left and in front of it the bay of Naples. This field is my favourite place in the world after home. I just love running down the hill through the long grass and woof woof as I go to show my contentment. I stop, turn round and look at Ami and woof woof again to say thank you to her for bringing me. Lilly loves it too when she comes, and we enjoy a race, a play or a game of tig as we descend.

When we get to the bottom of the hill, we go down some steps and then turn right to  go along another little lane which brings us to a big, wooden door and adjacent to this, there is an iron gate. If we want to take a shortcut to our garden, I go through the bars of the gate while Ami climbs over the adjoining wall. The owners of this garden are never around and don't mind us just popping through.

Going this way makes sure I don't put on any extra weight, otherwise I wouldn't be able to get through the bars. Once after Christmas I tried to get through the gap and nearly got stuck. I couldn't make it so had to reverse and try another one. It must have been one or two milli- metres wider, so breathing in I just about managed to squeeze through. No indulging next Christmas!

Sometimes when Ami and Francesco have got a free day we go further afield for a walk, and obviously that is even more exciting for me because I come across new and different smells.

At the same time though it can be a bit nerve racking …. that smells like a very big and ferocious dog, I hope I don't meet him! Well, on one of the walks it was a her, and to get past her it was touch and go. This old, unhappy, cantankerous female ran for me and even Ami and Francesco were a bit scared. The problem was, we had to return the same way, but luckily she was sleeping. So, silently Ami picked me up and ran past the dog's house and up the hill to safety, hoping not to wake her up. We were successful and just had to wait for Francesco to follow on as quickly as he could with the problem he has with his knees.

That was an adventure that nobody wants to repeat, therefore we have not gone on that walk again. Was I glad to get back home!

Since I was a little pup Ami and Francesco have taken me out with them in the car and then for a walk to some very beautiful places, so picturesque that of course photos had to be taken, not only of the lovely views, but of me as well. At first, I wasn't too keen on having my photo taken, camera shy I was they say, but with time I got more used to it.

Yes, I can definitely say I'm a very lucky boy who has been to many places that some of the local humans haven't even visited, such as Positano, Montepertuso and Nocelle. They are villages on the famous Amalfi Drive and are visited every year by thousands of people from all over the world, and I've been to them!

As far as posing for photos though, you can see that I'm not very good.

I'm either not looking in the right direction or yawning my head off. It's such a bore having photos taken.

I'm a bit better in these.

What a beautiful place I live in!

And then I mustn't forget the times we go out for breakfast, lunch or an aperitif in a nice, dog friendly cafe or restaurant, so definitely not a bad life. Even Lilly came with us once.

So, to get back to my daily routine, in the evening I have my dinner which is of course one of the best moments of the day. When Ami is preparing it I get quite excited and hop about not knowing which paw to raise to say please, so first the right then the left but very quickly making it look like a little dance. When it is placed in front of me I get told to eat my vegetables and not make a mess. Even though I'm a boy I'm very ladylike when it comes to eating my dinner. I start taking small pieces from around the edge and eventually lick my dish clean if I've enjoyed it.

Lilly, on the other hand gobbles up anything that she has been offered as if there is no tomorrow, and then sits and watches me eating mine, waiting for any opportunity to help me finish it. If I've been given pasta which is not my favourite, I will probably leave it in my dish, until Ami tells me to eat everything up. I try, but it just won't go down the red lane, so rather than get into trouble I take each individual piece out into the garden and bury it, but purposely without memorizing where it is as I never want to dig it up again.

I usually have rice with my meat and sometimes the grains fall out of my mouth onto the floor.

-Look at all this mess! - Ami says. -Clean it up!-

So, I reluctantly go back and eat up all that has fallen on the floor, it isn't really that tasty without the meat which I finished first, but I don't want to be shouted at again for making a mess. It's amazing though that sometimes I hear Ami's students ask her for the  meaning of the word "mess", and I already know it!

After dinner it's time for a little play in the garden or indoors with my rag, sock, rope, ball or soft toy. If Ami and Francesco are playing cards by the fire in winter, I love to interrupt them as much as possible, so take my toys to them to make them play with me, then all of a sudden, I just crash out on the carpet until someone wakes me up because I've been snoring.

When I was little, I used to have a nurse, but now I'm grown up I prefer to just lie down on the carpet or sit by the fire in the winter.

When Ami and Francesco go to bed, I do too. It's been a long day and I'm very tired.

Goodnight.

The coronavirus time

As I've often mentioned, I live in an international, hi-tech family, made up of different nationalities and where there are a lot of comings and goings with Victoria living away from home in London. She often returns for a holiday, and of course Amy goes to London to visit her or Southbourne to visit Nana and naturally Nana or Amy's friends come over to stay with us. Consequently, there are often suitcases being brought in or taken out.

This of course goes on together with Amy's job of teaching English to all her students who come and go on a more regular basis, usually once a week. So, there are a lot of different smells to sniff on all the different cars that bring and fetch them.

Is it possible for you to believe that this all of a sudden just immediately stopped completely? Basically, from one day to the next! No visitors, no students, no cars, and not even Amy around.

She had left early one morning when it was still cold and dark with her big suitcase, and as usual when she was going far away, she told me to be a good boy for Francesco, eat my vegetables and not bark during the night, or sleep on the sofa and that she would see me soon. Soon!!!! Nearly 8 weeks had gone by and still no sound of her, where on earth was she? What on earth was she doing? Had she and Francesco separated, and would Victoria and I have to decide who to go and live with?

I did speak to her on the phone or on WhatsApp though, she called my name, whistled me, or told me to go and get my ball or my rope! How ridiculous! How can I play ball or rope on a phone?

But they were not the only changes at this peculiar time. Francesco was always at home, he was never going to work on his new scooter, and on the odd occasion he did go out with the supermarket bag to get the shopping, he wore this light blue mask over his face.

Then, when the neighbours stopped to chat, they would stand away from Francesco as if he had a terrible disease. I eventually learned that it was a kind of virus going around the world, and unfortunately, and very sadly, it was killing lots and lots of people. Lilly was very knowledgeable on the subject because she spent so much time in front of the television when the news was on. She told me that the humans were not allowed out except for emergencies to prevent the virus from spreading as it was so contagious.

In fact, she told me that a lot of our doggie friends who lived in flats were having more walks than usual, the humans were allowed out to walk their dogs, so it was a good excuse for them to have to get out of the same old four walls. Of course, for Lilly and I nothing was different, we were free to come and go as always, but Amy wasn't around to take us to the fields which I was a bit sad about. Francesco took me sometimes, but not every day. When would this strange period end? When would Ami return? When would life get back to normal again?

The rescued Romanian dog

As I've often said I'm a very modern, up to date dog who uses WhatsApp. From an early age when Victoria left home to go and live in London, she would video call and after she had spoken to her parents, it would be my turn. I could understand what she was saying but was very shy to actually look at her on the screen.

Sometimes it was Amy who was not at home, so I would hear her voice on Francesco's telephone asking me if I'd been a good boy, and where my rope and ball were. Again, I wouldn't look at her, but I knew what she was talking about.

It was very interesting on one occasion when Amy was in England visiting her mum and she was telling Francesco about meeting a very nice lady and her dog.

Apparently, as Ami was walking down to the beach, she saw a dog who was so like me that she just had to stop, say hello and stroke the dog. After getting the ok from the owner Ami petted and spoke gently to this lovely, soft little girl realizing how much she was missing me and while doing  so she explained to the elderly owner that I was very, very similar, but a boy, a little bigger and also that I was a very long way away in It-aly.

Ami continued to explain that she was in the UK to assist her mum who had to undergo quite a serious operation in hospital and was hoping to stay for a number of weeks to help her get back to normal.

The lady was very sympathetic and told Ami that her beautiful dog's name was Toffee and that she had adopted her from Romania where she had been a street dog, therefore no home or family to look after her. That is very sad, isn't it?

One of her granddaughters had gone to the country to fetch the little puppy for her grandmother, who had recently suffered a great loss when her husband died. So, Toffee helped provide some company and comfort to the lady and filled in her days with little walks. It was also a happy ending for Toffee who had a new home in a new country and was loved and being well looked after.

There was only one problem and that was that Toffee could not be let off her lead because she chased bikers and joggers. On Southbourne beach there are a lot of both and unfortunately this incorrect behaviour could lead to an accident. How can this problem be solved?? Very easily!!! Toffee was going to Dog School to learn not to do this!

"Fancy that!", I thought, dogs going to school!!!

A great surprise

It was the 20th of June 2020, the pandemic year and in the morning, I noticed a lot going on. Francesco was cleaning all the house and watering the garden, making everything look nice, and then he went out in the car. That gives me the chance to go and visit Lilly when no one is at home, even though I'm really supposed to stay to look after it.

After I had been at Lilly's house for a while I started listening for the tooting of the horn of my car. I can detect its particular sound even when it is almost a kilometre away you know. We dogs have very good hearing! A long time went by, but eventually there it was beeping before coming round the last bend before the straight part of the lane to our house. Off I went, galloping through Lilly's garden, past the hens, over the wall and through the hole in the fence. I had just about made it home as the car turned into the drive. Well, you see, really, it's our job to stay at home and guard the house, that's why some people have a dog, a guard dog. It wasn't really the case for me, but Francesco does tell me to stay at home and look after the house before going out. It's just a bit boring and sometimes I get lonely, so I skive off to see my friends and make sure I'm back before they arrive, so they don't know!!!!

The car stopped in front of the house and Francesco got out. But there was somebody else there too, who was it? Who could it be? I couldn't believe it!!! Who was it getting out of the car? After four months away, which was totally unprecedented, it was Ami!!! I went up to her and she had that familiar English smell on her, but why had she been away so long?

Well, it didn't matter, she was here now and talking to me, stroking my head and making a big fuss of me, that's all that mattered. I was over the moon, and when this great surprise had sunk in, I had a little run around her, almost a canter and as I did so I yelped as if I was a three-month old puppy again. I was just sooooo happy!

After Ami's return, life didn't exactly return to how it was about half a year ago. I was now used to following Francesco around all day, and I had also taken up the habit of sleeping on a rug next to Francesco's bed, but Ami didn't mind any of this. Eventually, I noticed a little bit of the old routine coming back into our lives. Francesco went to work on his motor scooter, and some boys and girls came for their English lesson which they had outside, they sat at one end of the table while Ami sat at the other. This was called social distancing, and they wore a face mask. And because they were outside, it meant that I couldn't do any barking!

-No barking during my lesson! - Ami would firmly pronounce.

Still, it was lovely to have her home, have her company, have my chest rubbed and go on our little walks together again. Everybody was blissfully happy. It seemed that the worst of this coronavirus thing was in the past, and that things could only get better.

Pandemic dogs

During this Coronavirus time I was often hearing some new words. I heard them when Francesco and Ami were speaking to each other, or when they were doing a video call with Victoria in London, from the television, everywhere! Epidemic, pandemic, Covid 19, contagious, cases, hospital, intensive care and lockdown. Lockdown? What was this word? What on earth did it mean?

Well, apparently, to stop this terrible virus from spreading people had to stay at home and not go out unnecessarily. Children had to do school lessons online at home and also grown-ups had to work from home when possible. This was called "smart working".

Of course, with this new situation pets where over the moon, well, us dogs anyway. We love to have company and somebody always at home. Some dogs that were usually left at home on their own for a good part of the day because their humans were at work now had their owners at home all day and every day. It was fantastic for them. Don't know about cats. They like to think they're superior to all overs and need nobody.

Anyway, during this lockdown period, even though people couldn't go out to do a lot of things, they were allowed to go for a walk locally, especially if they had a dog to walk. Another reason why we dogs were so happy. Instead of one walk a day, some of us were getting two or three!!!! Great!

Also, during this time, because people were at home and had a lot more free time due to lockdown, lots of puppies were adopted, the humans were bored and so wanted a new interest. This was very happy news, but unfortunately for some it didn't always end in a good way. When lockdown ended and people could resume their old routine, the poor dogs were left for hours all alone in the house which of course they were not used to. We don't like to be alone; we love human company and to follow our owners around all day to be with them.

Another problem that arose during this lockdown period was that some dogs had been fed far too much while all the family had been at home and had to go on a diet. It is obviously very important to feed us the right quantity of food, not too little, but not too much either and not be too generous or spoil us by giving us a lot of treats. They are bad for us.

So, the pandemic also had consequences on us too, some positive but unfortunately some negative as well.

I would just like to mention another point too, and that is when you are thinking of adopting a little puppy, a very, very important thing to remember and to take into consideration is that it is for life and we can live up to eighteen years, or in some cases even longer. For this amount of time, we need to be loved and looked after, fed, watered, taken to the vet and walked. We're not like a toy that when you have played with it several times the novelty wears off, so it is placed in the toy cupboard and forgotten about. No. We want to become part of the family and live happily with our humans. It is therefore a decision to be taken seriously as it is quite a commitment, but of course all the love, cuddles, licks and loyalty that we give in return have no price!

The pandemic continues

Come September things seemed to be normal, the little children who live near me started going to school, walking past my house early in the morning all fresh and bright with their new school rucksacks on their backs, and some students came home for English lessons with Ami. Then, just as we were getting used to this autumnal routine, things changed dramatically. Nobody walked past the house, no students arrived for their lesson, and Francesco didn't go to work anymore.

Apparently, we were in lockdown again. That is when you have to stay at home to prevent the naughty virus from spreading from one person to another. Oh well, no problem for me, in fact it's much better because with Francesco at home there are more interesting things to do with him. Going round the garden, collecting the eggs in the hen house and catching any mice we may see there too, I really love that!!!! Sometimes Francesco gives me an egg. I really want one at first, but then when I've got it, I don't quite know what to do with it. I hold it in my mouth and look at him for advice. He takes it from me, breaks it into my dish and I eat it up. Very tasty!

Francesco would sometimes let the hens out so they could have a wander around the garden. They love doing that and all stick together and go around the garden in the same direction every time, happy to be on nice, fresh ground full of yummy things to scratch up and eat. As the daylight diminishes in the late afternoon, the hens start to head home to their house, and it was Francesco's job to put them in, count them, and finally shut the door. Of course, I am there to help, though I don't think I'm very good at it. I think I stand in the wrong place, because instead of going into their house, the hens run off in the opposite direction, and Francesco gets very angry and bellows at me. I don't mind, I have a whale of a time, but when Ami does it, I'm very good because she only allows me to stand behind her, so we get the job done in seconds.

Ami and I only do it occasionally though, because although her students weren't coming in person for their lessons, I heard her talking to them on the computer, doing an online lesson. This was new to her, something that she had to learn, and she set up everything she needed on the table in the living room, right next to my bed. A bit inconvenient really for Francesco and I, because he had to go to the bedroom to watch tv, and during a lovely deep sleep I was often woken up only to be told to stop snoring, she couldn't hear her student. Or she would be saying to her student that if they could hear any funny noises it wasn't her stomach but me snoring. Apparently, it was the only place in the house where the internet connection was good, so Francesco and I had to just get on with it.

This lockdown continued more or less until Christmas when, although we couldn't have lots of people round like the other time, at least Victoria came. No problem for me though. There were still lots of tasty bits going and nice long walks all together, but thank goodness that marathon wasn't on! Do you remember? Better to be by the fire!

Friends and fights

I have a few good dog friends, Lilly, Chestnut and Bella, and have known all three of them since I was a little puppy, but my very best friend is Lilly. We love each other dearly and do many activities together like lying in the sun, looking for lizards in the flower beds, eating, drinking, having a pet from Ami, inspecting the apartment upstairs, waiting to come in, chasing something after hearing a mysterious noise, though first of all I look at Lilly to see in which direction we have to run.

Then we go for a walk together with Ami and Francesco, and finally the tastiest of them all…waiting for the sausages to cook on the open fire with Victoria.

Yes, we really do get on well together, rarely does a day go by that we don't see each other, either at my house or at Lilly's. And even though Lilly is probably at the good old age of 15, she's still often ready for a little game of tig in the garden or biting, that is like pretending to have a fight.

It's one thing pretending to have a fight, and another when it is actually real. My brother Dodo had been adopted into a family near me and although we'd cuddled up to the same mummy and had lived our early puppyhood together, once we had left our birth home we detested each other and if we came face to face on a walk, both of us would have to be picked up by our owners to save us from having a big dog fight. I don't know why we had developed this dislike for each other but fortunately the problem was solved when Dodo and his family moved to another village, and I have never seen him again.

However, we could say he was replaced by another small, black dog which lived next door to Lilly and that I would see when using the short cut through a garden to get to my house. In this area of Italy, the land is often terraced and he lived in the garden below while we walked past his property on the above land. He did not like this at all and barked and growled not wanting us to pass, but of course was of no threat because there was quite a high embankment that separated the two gardens on the two levels. Of course, on this occasion I was in my element showing how brave and courageous I could be and enjoyed running backwards and forwards along the grassy edge barking my head off at him even though Ami had told me to stop. I knew that I was completely safe, that in no way this dog could get me, until one day, what happened? I fell down into his garden.

I thought there was land under the grassy edge, but in fact there was nothing and plonk I went to find myself face to face with my enemy. I was having kittens as they say, and Ami was petrified we were going to have an all-out fight. I think maybe the fact that I all of a sudden arrived right in front of this dog, must have put him into shock because fortunately he became quiet and motionless. Perhaps he thought I was Tyson the flying dog and had other special powers up my sleeve which I was about to use on him, so he decided to surrender. The problem was, how was I going to get back up to Ami and then home?

Ami always has the solution to any problem and told me to walk straight on along this kind of drive in the black dog's garden to the road and then come through the bars in the iron gate into the garden where she was. Do you know, I did it! I understood every word she said and we were soon back home safe and sound. What an experience that was!

Have you heard of taking revenge? It was to come to me. Usually, this black dog is in his garden behind a big gate, but on one day as I was just coming round the corner ready to go through the bars of the gate that takes us into our short cut, he was there on this side of the gate, totally free and he ran up to me menacingly. I kind of ran backwards and would you believe fell into a little gap between a wall and a fence. I was trapped and the black dog looked down at me from above growling as if to say:

"Now it's my turn to be above you. How are you going to get out of this, you little rascal?".

Ami was there again to help me. She shooed the dog away, pulled me out of this kind of crevice, and we rushed home to safety.

We have met since then and I'm happy to say that after we both had a good sniff of each other, nothing happened, and we walked on quite peacefully. I suppose I could say we had made friends. Wouldn't it be wonderful if this could happen between humans too, forgive and forget about previous disputes and walk on happily.

I am, however, not usually very sociable with other dogs when I meet one on my walk. Actually, I'm often a little nervous and worry about walking past a strange dog, Ami usually has to coax me on. This is due to some scary experiences I've had in the past since I was a little puppy.

Now I will tell you about the time I came face to face with Julius. I don't know who he thought he was, roaming around on my road.

"I'll see you off!", I thought to myself as Ami and I were returning from a walk and he was there near my aunty's house. As I was nearly on our drive, I was not on my lead so was able to frantically run up to him, barking and growling and wanting a fight. Julius was on a lead, and it was a good job really as he was much bigger than me and stronger.

His owner pulled him away from me, that saved me getting my head bitten off. Ami shouted at me to leave him alone and in the end, I did as I was told, but it didn't finish there as in fact Ami was furious with me because Julius had just been minding his own business. She threw the lead at me and told me to go home straight away. I did! The lead didn't catch me as Ami is not a very good thrower, but just the sound of it landing on the ground near me made me jump, so with my tail between my legs, I ran as fast as I could to be safe in my basket at home.

Some weeks later would you believe we had another encounter! Julius was coming round the corner of the narrow lane where the Madonnina is. We were both on leads, so theoretically there shouldn't have been any problem. But what happened? Julius obviously remembered the last time I had instigated the ruffle, so he looked at me disapprovingly thinking I was not going to get away with it lightly this time, pulled on his lead and all of a sudden was out of his harness!

He was so big, towering over me, I snapped back, but remember I don't have a full set of adult teeth, so these little ones don't have much effect. Ami was trying to get me away, Julius's owner was trying to pull him back, then suddenly I was up high, on a wall. Ami had managed to pick me up and save me. My goodness, that was a close one, we were all shaking like leaves after that, me the most but also Ami and Julius's owner. I suppose it had been my fault on that previous walk interfering with him... Dogs don't forget!

The world is a beautiful, wonderful place, but sometimes nature can be cruel, unfair and savage. While we are talking about fights, I would just like to give you all some advice on how to deal with us naughty dogs when we see red and become angry.

Of course, there are many reasons why we fight, like you humans, but most commonly it's to protect our territory or our young or our owners.

I remember seeing a very violent fight between two females, fighting to protect their territory. The humans were having a struggle to separate and stop the dogs, and it can be dangerous for them to get too close as they could also get bitten. What is the best thing to do? Throw a bucket of water over them or use a large object such as a chair to divide them. Fortunately, this fight ended without any major consequences.

A meeting with a new dog

It has been known that one of Ami's student's parents have come to collect their child and with them in the car there is a dog. It's not usually let out of the car, but just to make sure it has no intention of doing so, I bark quite determinedly to emphasize the fact it is not welcome to venture into my garden.

But what do you do when it's one of the little neighbours who comes up my drive with a tiny, lively, curious, thing on a lead with sharp teeth? This happened recently, I was beside myself! It was tiny and so quick running around my legs wanting to smell me, lick me and play. I didn't!

Ami stroked me and talked to me and was ready to hold me back should I have decided to see this overgrown mouse off. You see, it's not for anything, but we get very jealous. What if Ami suddenly fell in love with this undisciplined but cuddly puppy, and didn't love me anymore? That's why she stayed very close to me and spoke softly to me, to reassure me that this would not happen.

Now Tano, the puppy, often passes my house and even comes to say "Hello!", but I understand he is no threat and my mummy and daddy, and Victoria are always going to love me! Even though I have to have the patience of a saint when he wants to smell me all over, or wants to play, for which I have no desire and the older I get, it is becoming less and less!

This gave me the experience to cope with another mat-ter and that was when we had some guests staying with us in our apartment upstairs who actu-ally had brought their dog for the hol-iday too. Never be-fore had this hap-pened, and never be-fore had I seen such a tiny, white hairy dog which looked like a kind of duster without the stick! I was not perturbed with the situation though and even allowed her into my garden and get near me.

As you can see from this photo, he was quite a cutie when his face wasn't covered with all that hair.

My predecessor

Has anyone ever called you by the wrong name? It's ok if it happens only once, isn't it? But often and it becomes a little frustrating and even annoying. It happens to me. I sometimes get addressed with a different name, Victoria, Francesco, Ami or Chloe. Chloe? Who's Chloe? Ok, the other three I know, but where does this Chloe come from? And it's a girl's name! I'm not a girl!!!

Eventually I found out that Chloe had been Ami and Francesco's beloved pet dog before I arrived and had been a member of their little family even before Victoria was born. Chloe had nearly lived to the grand age of eighteen, in fact they were going to have a special eighteenth birthday party for her when sadly she suddenly died. At the time Ami and Victoria were in London celebrating Nana's eightieth birthday, so you can imagine how they both felt when they returned, and Chloe was no longer there to greet them.

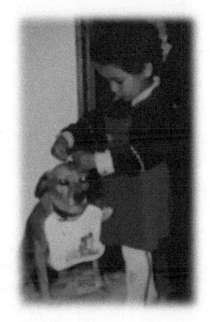

However, she had had a very good life, especially as she was able to see and enjoy Victoria grow up from a baby into a young woman. I didn't have this opportunity as Victoria was already twenty years old when she adopted me, and then soon after, she left to live in London. Old photos of Chloe show how dedicated and patient she had been with little Victoria, my favourite is this one of Chloe having a bib tied around her.

I am very pleased to say though, that I too have recently had the pleasure of spending time with a little girl who lives very near me. It was when Ami was away visiting Victoria and Nana in the UK and Francesco was at work every afternoon that I was getting a little bit bored and lonely staying at home. I would have normally gone to Lilly's house, but it was very hot, and her house is further away from this little girl's, who basically lives next door. So, I thought why not? I'll go to there! I got a warm welcome and stayed until early evening when Francesco returned from work. The following day, I went again and enjoyed being there so much that I continued to make daily visits.

They have a very pleasant garden, similar to ours really with some soft grass to lie on and plenty of shade, so I was able to do like I do at home on a hot summer's day, lie in the sun, then move and plonk myself down somewhere in the shade to cool off, go back into the sun again to warm up and so on.

But in between all this, the little girl whose name is Sara and I made friends. She had always been a bit hesitant to touch me or pat me on my head, but gradually became more confident and was pleasantly surprised to see how soft my fur was on my head, face and ears. Softer than Lilly's apparently. We also sometimes played ball together, and I was over the moon that I too had a little friend. Like Chloe had been able to enjoy being with Victoria when she was young, I was having a similar experience with little Sara. Her parents were also very friendly towards me and always said hello to me when they passed my house.

So, when at Christmas time Ami and Francesco went to stay with Nana and Victoria, I went to stay with Sara and her family. My basket was taken into their house and placed near the front door, and like at home, I did a couple of woofs and they opened the front door to let me in, I hopped into my basket and slept until the morning. When Ami and Francesco returned, they were told that I had been a very good boy, very well behaved and Sara's mother said that I had even been more obedient than little Sara, but she was only joking. What lovely neighbours we have!

It is lovely for little ones to have a pet around them. It has many benefits, the list is too long to mention them all, but perhaps the most important one is learning something about the animal world.

At this point of my story, I have a confession to make. I have talked about my life and adventures with my family, but in fact there was another member that I have not mentioned, and I now feel very guilty about this. Lilly the cat, please accept my apologies and forgive me. Yes,

Lilly was already the family, pet cat when I was adopted, but you know what cats are like, they consider themselves so important and much more superior to us, and usually keep themselves to themselves that I just forgot to include her in my tale.

Of course, you can imagine that she was absolutely horrified when I came to live in her house, so she kept her distance and refused to have anything to do with me, even though I was all for a play. If I dared to venture close to her though, to give her a sniff or a lick, her paw would be raised and come hard onto my face to discourage me from doing anything of the kind again.

She was always so grumpy with a miserable face on her all the time, probably because she also had to tolerate Lilly the dog, who had been around before me as well. It was a little bit confusing with all these Lilly's, but Lilly the cat had come first. Whilst Ami was gardening one day Tommaso the neighbour, who was on the other side of the fence said to Ami that he wanted to introduce his newly adopted puppy to her and when she discovered that her name was Lilly, she started calling her saying for example:

-What a lovely girl you are, Lilly! Come here Lilly! - and so on.

Lilly the cat, who was also in the garden at the time, came running up to Ami thinking she was giving all these kind words to her, but as she got nearer and realized Ami's attention was not on her but on a four-legged, brown creature that she was holding in her arms, she abruptly came to a halt, was highly offended and took an immediate dislike to this new neighbour.

In the following weeks to come Lilly the dog was not at all shy and would quite happily spend the afternoon at our house. I remember Ami saying sometimes that it was lovely having her, because she was there for a bit of company and a cuddle, but then would go to her own home to be fed etc. I don't think our Lilly shared the same opinion! Then I came along, and it was probably the last straw for Lilly the cat, yet another dog and a young and lively one too.

However, she had been in my position with Chloe, that is Chloe was already the pet dog and Lilly the cat came as a new arrival, and so being very young she was lively and playful towards Chloe who, however, accepted her quite quickly without any fuss. So, now it was her turn to accept me, and I must admit it took some time but eventually she did, and we became brother and sister. Of course, she always maintained her superior position to me, for example she was able to sit on the armchair

and from high up looked down at me clearly ordering me to stay where I was on the floor.

They say "time" is the cure for everything and in my case, it was certainly true, as Lilly the cat gradually began to

accept me and we would even play hide and seek together. She would go to hide, and me having no idea   where she was, would go running round the corner only to be frightened out of my skin when she jumped out at me.

I don't know whether I found it particularly enjoyable really because if she caught you with her claws, it hurt a lot, but Ami and Francesco always found the scene very amusing.

Yes, I can honestly say that she wasn't really grumpy and miserable all the time, it was just the way God had made her mouth but, in fact, she was quite a good sport even allowing Victoria to dress her up.

 She was also quite an intellect and enjoyed reading Nana's English newspaper when she could. I don't think she used to do the crossword puzzle like Nana did though.

Unfortunately, she's no longer with us, so I have taken over that superior position, and will also sit on the armchair and the sofa when nobody's around.

The three-legged dog

The only dog I play with is my great friend Lilly. When I was a puppy, she was like a babysitter to me and would play with me for hours. Ami was always happy when she came because it meant I didn't get into mischief in the house while she was doing her lessons. Now Lilly's older but we will still sometimes have a good race around the garden or play catch. It's usually my idea to play, I start nipping her legs, looking her in the eye, giving her a little bark which in dog language means, "Come on, let's have a play!"

I can run really fast, so can Lilly, but she tires before me. If Francesco is at home, he always tells me to slow down as I could hurt myself. A bit of a spoil sport really, but he's only concerned about me. Unfortunately, it was proved that he was right and one day I DID hurt myself!

Ami had left a sunbed out and as I was going eighty km around the fruit trees on the lawn, ready to jump off the little garden wall, I couldn't because the sunbed was there, so I kind of ran on that and then fell off it. At first, all seemed good, but later on I couldn't walk on my back leg, good job I had another three! After a few days of being a three-legged dog, I was taken to the Vet's. I had injured my knee, could possibly need to have an operation! My goodness, that made me shake even more than usual on the Vet's cold stainless-steel table!

Ami didn't take me on such long walks after that, and I wasn't allowed to run or jump. Then I had to take another kind of pill which I managed to spit out sometimes like all the others, so again it was wrapped up in something tasty to help it down the red lane.

A couple of days later, I noticed that Francesco also began taking MY pills as he had knee problems too. Even though the Vet had prescribed them for me they were actually for humans and certainly helped both of us.

Ami started taking us out on short walks, which in actual fact, I enjoyed more when Francesco was with us because we were able to take it easy, without rushing, and I think this gentle stroll together with the occasional massage that Amy gave me really helped my knee to recover. Although it took quite a while, fortunately it eventually got better, I didn't need to have an operation and once again became a four-legged dog, that could run fast and jump.

This is the sunbed, but rather than falling off it, I'm having a nice lie on it.

I can also tell you a story about this sunbed and its origin. You would never guess where it came from!

It all happened a long time ago when I was a young puppy on one of our first trips to the beach. As I've already mentioned I'm not a great fan of water and don't want to really get my feet wet, let alone swim and get all my body wet. On this particular occasion it was warm enough to go swimming, because first of all Amy went for a swim and I cried and whimpered on the seashore wanting her back on the beach near me, and then when she returned it was Francesco's turn and I stayed with Amy. I wasn't so perturbed about Francesco, but every so often looked out at sea for him.

He had gone fishing so would probably be a while, but all of a sudden, I saw him. He was pulling this great big, heavy red thing out of the sea. It wasn't a fish but the sunbed that is now in our garden. This was actually quite typical of Francesco when he went fishing, to find various things like goggles, bracelets, a beach towel and now we can add to the list a sunbed. Occasionally though, he also caught a fish to show us, before throwing it back. Oh well, as long as I had a towel to lie on, I don't suppose I minded waiting for him.

Family life

I felt a little tension in the air the other day, you know we dogs are very good at understanding how our humans are feeling, if they are happy, relaxed, worried, anxious, sad, down in the dumps, in a good mood or in a bad mood, or ill. The other day I could sense that Ami was deeply worried about something and a bit sad, although she tried her best to hide it and get on with all her chores in the house and garden.

I try to be as supportive as possible in such circumstances and follow her around everywhere to be with her, although on this occasion I did get asked to move half a dozen times as she was vacuuming; I had just got nice and comfy on the carpet and there's an:

-Excuse me! - shouted at me.

The same thing happened in the garden when she was weeding, wherever I decided to have a little lie down seemed to be just where she wanted the wheelbarrow to go, and I had to move!

But I can understand how she feels on certain days especially with Nana and Victoria being so far away. Even I get to feel a little down in the dumps when Ami and Francesco are on holiday, even though I am being well looked after.

Anyway, on this particular day I noticed that Amy was on the phone in the morning to Nana. They usually speak in the evening after my walk and dinner, so it was a bit odd that they were speaking in the morning too, but I perceived that Ami was worried about her mum, after all she is over the age of ninety and lives a very long way away. So probably she just wanted an extra chat to her, to make sure everything was as good as it could be.

I know all about Nana's age because Ami made a special birthday card for her ninetieth birthday. One day she placed some photos on the grass probably to give a nice green background and then took a photo of them using her phone. I was also in the garden, observing all that was going on and thought that I'd like to be in the photo too. So, I lay down with my nose right next to the photos.

-You're being very nosey - Ami told me.

But she sent the photo of my nose together with the others to Nana, as she knew that I too would want to wish her a happy 90th birthday.

All in all, wouldn't it be wonderful if we could all live together under the same roof? I would have more people to play with me and even take me for walks, I wouldn't have to wait so long for somebody to open the front door for me, and somebody would always be free to rub my chest. I'm quite a sociable boy and enjoy people around me as long as when I want a sleep, they don't disturb me and I'm always happy and in a good mood.

Like you humans we dogs all have our own personality, I suppose, besides being sociable, two characteristics

 that stand out for me are that I'm quite sensitive, so easily get offended if someone raises their voice to me and I'm not very brave. If I hear a noise from outside in the evening, I will bark but will stand back for Ami to go out first, and then I'll follow her. I'm a little possessive as well, I don't like other dogs getting too friendly with my family, and of course I will show Lilly my teeth if she gets too near my dinner and naturally, I don't want other male dogs in my garden or near my house.

There is one which lives a couple of gardens away which will dare to come and wee near my front door would you believe! On these occasions I must say I am very brave because I will snarl, growl and snap at him viciously and he will run away squealing and whimpering as if I'd bitten him ferociously. Once even Ami came running out of the house after hearing him thinking that I'd nearly killed him, the noise he made. And after all this he always has the audacity to come back and repeat his actions. It is so infuriating!

So, what about the humans I live with? What are their personalities like? Well, first of all Francesco is always happy whistling away, oh except when I don't do what I'm told with the hens, he then becomes furious and bellows at me but I'm enjoying being with the hens so much that I don't take it to heart, and he's only angry with me for a moment.

He's often ready to play a joke, like putting his sunglasses on me, but he also gives me treats.

When he had a Vespa, he used to take me for a little ride on it. That was amazing!

He doesn't have a Vespa anymore, so it's a ride in the wheelbarrow, but I don't mind... the most important thing is for me to be with him, helping with all the garden chores. I don't know how he'd manage without me!!!!

What about Victoria? She too is a very cheerful person, always smiling and laughing and often ready for a game of hide and seek in the house.

She loves calling me with a new name, the latest was "Mingy", but don't ask me why, I have no idea! She's also very affectionate with me, giving me a nurse, allowing me on the sofa near her, or picking me up.

Finally, there's Amy. Although she is usually quite cheerful, she is probably more serious than the other two but is also very affectionate and loving to me, stroking my head, cuddling me, kissing me, rubbing my chest and telling me often that I am her lovely boy. She also loves teasing me though, calling Francesco her "lovely boy" right in front of me purposely to make me jealous. I look at her sadly and if she doesn't stop go and stand between the two of them just to remind her that I exist too.

In addition to this she loves imitating me when I yawn or sneeze. Ever since I was a little pup, I've been allergic to dust, vehicle fumes and smoke, so I quite often have to sneeze. Ami copies my sneeze which makes me sneeze again and so on until I do a small, high-pitched whimper to beg her to stop. It's a good job Francesco is around and tells her to stop making fun of me. She then gives me a kiss  and cuddle and tells me that I am her beautiful boy!

The yoga dog

One of the best things to do when a person is feeling a little anxious or uptight is yoga. In actual fact, we dogs practise it daily. When we wake up in the morning or after a little nap, we always stretch our neck, nice and long, and the yoga position called downward facing dog is because we often do it to stretch our backs. These are some of the positions that you humans have copied from us.

I remember when Ami started doing yoga because all of a sudden this blue mat appeared out of nowhere and when it was rolled out, guess what, I was NOT allowed on it! I thought it had been bought especially for me as it was blue, and when I surreptitiously put a paw on it and found out how soft and foamy it was, I imagined how comfortable it would be to lie on in the garden instead of on the hard concrete of the patio. But it was only for Ami, I was told again and again, she could go on it doing her downward facing dog, bridge pose, cat and cow and warrior one, two and three etc, but me, not even a paw! Still, I really enjoyed lying right by the side of the mat purposely getting in the way, and even when Ami asked me to move, I wouldn't! Once when I was right near her, I even snapped at her, which of course got me into a lot of trouble.

Well, I thought she was going to attack me as in her downward facing dog position all of a sudden, she did a loud angry sounding lion's breath out. This is when you breathe out noisily to empty all your lungs of oxygen and release any tensions, and at the same time stick your tongue out. It has a similar sound to a growl and with this strange expression on Ami's face with her tongue stuck out, I just got a fright and thought she was about to attack me like a lion. So, I had to defend myself, didn't I? Anyway, no harm done but since that incident I am not allowed to sit anywhere near the mat.

So, watching her from afar going through her movements I used to think what a waste of time all this yoga was, and how she could be doing something more enjoyable, like playing rag with me. Well, that too is a kind of exercise, isn't it? In fact, I often brought my rag or sock to her when she was doing her cat and cow pose, to which she abruptly replied:

-Later, when I've finished!-

When Francesco was at home, he tried to encourage me to do the same movements as Ami was doing, you know there are these super, clever dogs who do yoga with their owners who you see on fb… No, that's too much of an effort for me, it's much more fun just being in the way and a nuisance.

At first, Ami used to go to someone's house to do this new hobby, and I know they had a dog because I could smell it on Ami's clothes when she returned. I wondered if he was well behaved during the lesson or a bit rebellious like me. Apparently, he was only a puppy and so very lively and wanted to sit on everyone's mat and play, but his owner, the yoga teacher, was gently training him to not bother her pupils and to sit on his own mat and either watch or sleep. He would get it in the end, I've no doubt about that.

During lockdown when nobody could go out, Ami started to follow another instructor on her iPad and actually still does today. She too has a big, grey dog called Benji who is very well behaved and just lies near his owner as she talks her pupils through the lesson. The teacher's name is Adrienne, and she is also very beautiful and even just hearing her voice I can tell that she is definitely a very dog-loving person.

She always includes Benji in her salutations and has such a soft, gentle but encouraging voice. I know Ami loves her even though she has never had the privilege of meeting her. Maybe one day, and then I could get to know Benji.

In any case, I can't emphasize enough how good it is for people to do yoga, for example, have you ever known a dog with a stiff neck? But apart from the physical benefits it also has many mental ones too. It makes your owners calmer, more patient, more reasonable and of a happier disposition and of course this can only make the pet's life better, can't it?

So, yoga for everyone I say,
if you haven't started yet,
start today!!
(I'm even becoming a poet!).

The unwanted birthday present

I'm not really too keen on the very hot weather we get in the summer here in Italy, especially in the months of July and August. It's so hot during the day that you can't really do much, even the humans just find somewhere cool to sit and, in the afternoon, they very often have a siesta, which is a sleep. For me, it's just a case of plonking myself down on the grass in the shade of the olive tree and then going into full sun until I get too hot and then back into the shade again, or I go into the house where it's quite cool.

It's too hot to go for a walk or catch lizards or even have a bark at any other dog that may pass the house, but then they don't come because it's too hot for them too. So, it's better for me to have a long siesta as well until about 6pm. Lizards, of course love this baking hot heat and come out to soak it all up. Even right by me!!!

However, there is one day during this hot period which is a little different, and that is Ami's birthday. Special tasty dishes are prepared for the outside evening buffet on the patio which family and friends are invited to, so also lots of tasty bits for me, and when the guests arrive there is usually someone who wants to play rag, rope or ball with me, so I have quite a pleasant time, together with going under the long tables to clear up anything anybody has dropped.

This year though, it was all very different. I kept hearing the word, "Positive". Victoria who was visiting was writing messages with this word in them and Ami was on the phone to people voicing the same one. What had happened? Did she mean positive to Covid, right on this special day? Unfortunately, she did. That is not a present anybody would want, is it? So, there was no party on this occasion, although some visitors did arrive just to say happy birthday, but they remained distant. If a person has Covid they have to practically isolate themselves from others to protect the others from getting it. So Ami, wearing a mask, was even sitting away from Victoria and Francesco.

What a peculiar evening! But it hadn't finished there. When it was bedtime, I, as usual went on the mat by the side of the bed where Francesco sleeps, ruffled it all up ready to settle down for the night when I suddenly realized that Ami was going to sleep in another room. That made it very complicated for me now, who should I go and sleep with, Francesco or Ami? They were usually together in the same room. I chose to go to Ami because I could sense she was a bit down in the dumps with this unwanted birthday present, and she had one of my favourite mats by her bed anyway, so I was still very comfortable.

This went on for quite a few evenings, I would go to Francesco, and Ami would call me to go there, then I would feel guilty not being by Francesco, but he didn't seem to mind. It just made me realize how difficult it must be for children whose parents are separated or divorced, to have to choose which one of them they want to be with. Luckily, in our family, this separation came to an end when I started hearing the word "negative". That was a happy word! At last, this nasty virus had obviously gone from Ami's body, and she was ok and was able to hug Victoria and Francesco once again. In actual fact, I had noticed how many more hugs, kisses and cuddles I was getting while she was positive obviously having to make up for the fact, she couldn't give any to Francesco and Victoria.

Luckily for Ami I can tolerate all this soppy stuff much more now than when I was younger and didn't like anybody near my face ready to kiss me. In fact, I often gave them my dirty look and showed them my teeth warning them that I would snap if they put any sloppy, wet lips on my cheek. I don't mind it too much these days but there is a limit, especially in the heat of the summer.

Time to say goodbye for now

Well, I think I've come to the end of my story, and I really hope you've enjoyed it. I've talked about the joys of having a pet, but at the same time the responsibility required to have one, my adventures, the time of the Coronavirus pandemic that we have lived through, and are still living through, and the wonderful life I have with my family.

We're all getting older now, Ami reached an important age on her last birthday, and Victoria will be coming up to her third decade soon. On the other hand, Francesco must still be quite young because he hasn't retired yet.

Little Lilly still comes to visit us every day, she too has all white hairs on her face and chin, but still likes a play every so often, and loves to be a part of our family. I get a bit jealous sometimes but am quite an easy going chap on the whole, so just accept her as one of us.

And finally, there's me. Yes, I suppose I'm getting on too. Victoria's been in London for nearly seven years now, and I was just a wee puppy of one year old when she went. So, how old does that make me in human years? Well, every human year is the equivalent of seven dog years, so eight times seven equals, my goodness, fifty-six. I'm middle aged!!!

In actual fact, the other day Ami started saying that I was a good MAN, instead of the usual good BOY... What had she said, a good MAN? But I suppose I'm not really a boy anymore, am I? I didn't like it though and gave her a dirty look.

She looked back at me lovingly with her smiling blue eyes and as I rolled onto my back, she gave my chest a rub like she often did and then said:

-Good MAN doesn't sound right, does it? Don't worry, you're my good BOY, and you will always be my good boy, forever and ever!-

I was very happy. Thank you for reading.

Tyson

Finito di stampare
nel mese di giugno 2023
presso Rotomail Italia S.p.A. – Vignate (MI)